Storyline

A Short Story Anthology

Selected by NEIL FULLER & PHILIP GARDNER

MACMILLAN

First published 1997 by
MACMILLAN EDUCATION AUSTRALIA PTY LTD
627 Chapel Street, South Yarra 3141
Reprinted 1998

Associated companies and representatives
throughout the world

National Library of Australia
cataloguing in publication data

Storyline: a short story anthology.

ISBN 0 7329 4156 3.

1. Short stories, English – 20th century. 2. Short stories,
Australian – 20th Century. I. Gardner, Philip. II. Fuller,
Neil, 1941–.

823.010809

Typeset in Giovanni Book by
Typeset Gallery, Malaysia

Printed in Malaysia

Designed by Raul Diche
Illustrated by Ann Stanhope
Cover design by Dimitrios Frangoulis

Contents

Acknowledgements

The authors and publishers are grateful to the following for permission to reproduce the following copyright material.

Errol Broome for story 'Thanks for Nothing'; Curtis Brown, Sydney, for story 'Who Wins, Zadig?' by Libby Hathorn from her *Who? Stories*; Brian Fraser for story 'Freddie Martin and the Shopping Machine' from his *Puffinalia, No. 8, 1979*; Greene & Heaton Limited for story 'Killer' by © Paula Gosling 1989; Hickson Associates for story 'The Boy Who Wouldn't Get Out of the Pool' by Libby Gleeson; David Higham Assoc. for poem 'Jack and the Beanstalk' by Roald Dahl from *Revolting Rhymes*; Macmillan UK for poem 'Flannan Isle' by Wilfrid Wilson Gibson from his *Collected Poems 1905–1925*; Nelson Australia for story 'Three Skeleton Key' by George G. Toudouze from *The Brighter Side of School* by Forrestal and Reid; Victor Gollancz for story 'Barker' by Peter Dickinson from *The Blue Hawk*; Scholastic Inc. for story 'The Cyclops' Cave' from *The Adventures of Ulysses* by Bernard Evslin © 1969; Penguin Books for extract from 'S.H.C.' (pp. 25–32) from *Martini on the Rocks* by Susan Gregory (Kestrel Books, 1994) © Susan Gregory, 1984; Learning Media for 'Yellow Belly' by Beverley Dunlop, first published in the *School Journal* and reproduced courtesy of the New Zealand Ministry of Education © Crown, 1977.

Preface

Our selections for *Storyline* are based on a mixture of personal tastes, judgement of literary merit and the likely appeal to junior secondary students.

Each story is accompanied by questions, writing activities and language activities. This means that the book can be used in different ways, depending on the teacher's purpose. The questions aim to check the students' understanding of the stories; the writing activities are intended to help the students to focus on particular elements in the stories, and to emulate these; the language activities aim to extend understanding of the role of language in making narratives work.

Of course, a skilled reading by the teacher, with the students having a copy of the text in front of them, can heighten both enjoyment and appreciation. After such a reading, teachers may prefer to conduct a class discussion of how the story is constructed. Although the questions are an obvious starting point for such a discussion, teachers may also use the words of Edgar Allen Poe, who was the first to define a set of rules for the short story form. He said that:

- ✪ it must create a single impression;
- ✪ it should be capable of being read at a single sitting;
- ✪ not a word must be irrelevant, for every word must contribute to the predesigned total effect of the author;
- ✪ even the opening sentence must initiate this predesigned effect and be developed unswervingly through the story;
- ✪ when the author achieves his climax, the story should end, with no further explanation or secondary effects;
- ✪ only characters that are absolutely essential to the predesigned effect should be introduced, and these only developed to the extent required by the story.

The first story in the collection – Paula Gosling's 'Killer' – provides an excellent example of this structure.

We hope that the activities will help to develop the students' critical understanding of the stories, and, most importantly, that students will find pleasure in reading the collection.

Killer

He hated her. He did.

Every morning when he left, she was there, staring out the window, waiting for him, watching him. And when he came home at night she was there again, black beady eyes following his every move. As if he would do anything to her.

As if he could.

They'd guess, wouldn't they?

Or would they?

Everybody thought he was so quiet, so polite. Hah!

Neighbours – what do they *really* know about one another? After all, they hadn't lived there long, he was still a mystery, he was sure of that.

Nobody knew his business. He kept to his routine, was always well mannered when he met one of them on the street. Some might know his name – the postman knew his name, of course – but not much else. He kept himself to himself and so did his woman. Dol knew her place.

She kept the house tidy, did the shopping, made sure he got his meals on time, made sure his life was comfortable, that was all he required of her. So she wasn't very pretty, and lacked imagination, so what? Dol suited him just fine. If home was dull, if the food was always the same on the same days, and the evenings decidedly lacking in novelty, what did it matter? It was a place to sleep.

And a place to hide, if necessary.

He had enough excitement outside home to satisfy him.

More than enough.

He was the Expert. He had a reputation downtown – where a reputation counted. He was the one They turned to when some little rat fink had squealed once too often, or maybe caused Somebody Important some damage. They didn't like damage, downtown. They didn't like trouble. But they liked him. He worked fast. Neat and quiet, that was his style. In and out, nothing flashy – and he never talked. Not once. They liked that, too. He had plenty of work, one way and another. He kept in shape. He was in control.

Dol knew the consequences if she stepped out of line – he'd walked out before and he was quite prepared to do it again if she said anything he didn't like.

Or worse. He could do worse.

Doing worse was his business, after all.

And it *was* his business – nobody else's.

Especially not that nosy old hen next door.

He didn't know much about her, it was true, but she seemed to want to know all about him, the way she watched, the way she stared, the way she clocked his comings and goings.

It wasn't so bad, at first.

At first he'd even felt a little sorry for her.

After all, she was a shut-in, that was clear. Always in the same window during the day, keeping an eye on the street, probably making up stories about everyone, probably putting two and two together in her twisted little mind, maybe even coming to conclusions.

She might come to a conclusion about him.

That was the worry.

But who could she tell, shut up like that?

Her companion, he supposed.

Would she be believed? Dol said she was a gossipy, nervy thing. Drove her companion and just about everybody else on the street crazy. Always chattering in that cracked, cranky little voice that went through you like a rusty knife. Always complaining about something. Shut-ins got like that, he knew, went a little funny, got excited over nothing, made things up to liven their dull lives. Most of what she said was pure nonsense, of course. Probably nobody would believe her.

But they might.

Putting two and two together, she might hit on the truth. Stories got around, after all.

He tried varying his hours, changing his routine, but it didn't seem to make any difference, she was always there, watching, watching, watching.

And it played hell with his concentration. In a profession as specialised as his, you had to keep in touch with all the customers all the time, keep the territory covered. They wanted to know they could count on him, or they might turn to another Firm.

The Business might die on him.

Some joke.

But by the time they'd been in the new house a few months, he knew he was going to have to do something about Mrs Murgatroyd. That was her name. He didn't know her first name – probably nobody did except that poor, haggard woman who looked after her. He'd heard her companion speaking to her one day, when the window was open a crack and he was passing.

Just passing.

Mrs Murgatroyd had been eyeing him suspiciously from under her wrinkled eyelids when her companion had startled her by asking if she wanted something to drink. Well, the fuss that started! Talk about screeching, you'd think the poor woman had asked her if she wanted to be skinned alive!

And all the time she was complaining and crabbing, Mrs Murgatroyd was watching him out of the corner of her eye, watching to see if he reacted to her little performance.

Well, maybe she was a mind-reader.

Because the thought of breaking the bones in that scrawny little neck was beginning to haunt him. The thought of scaring the wits out of her, or even crushing the life right out of her body, kept him awake nights. He did it to others, in a professional way. Why not to her?

But it was only a thought.

Until she began to chatter at him through the glass, telling him off and screeching straight at him. That did it. That was the last straw. Staring was one thing, but jabbering at him another. It made him cringe every time he passed by.

What the hell would people think?

What was she saying?

What did she know?

He couldn't stand it. He knew he'd have to put a stop to it before it went on much longer. She was driving him crazy, and soon it might get back to Dol. He didn't want Dol upset.

Not again.

They'd had to move house twice before when neighbours

got suspicious about him, began to point the finger or whisper behind their hands. They seemed to think he was bringing his work home, one way or another. As if he would. Dol had denied everything, of course, she was loyal through and through. She loved him. And he loved her, too, in his way.

But, in the end, they'd had to move.

Well, he was through moving. He liked it here, it was quiet and there were fields to walk in nearby, and he'd really taken to it.

Except for Mrs Murgatroyd, of course.

The thing was, he'd have to wait his chance, move on impulse, trust his instinct. It wasn't professional, it was personal. Which meant no set-up, no back-up, no inside information. Not kill-to-order, and nothing to swell the kitty, afterwards. Not with this one. There had to be no connection with him, that was the thing. No way anyone could guess that he had anything to do with it.

Not easy.

Waiting never is, no matter how much of it you do.

But then, one morning, the moment arrived. All unexpected, the way these things do. He had slept a little late, and left the house just in time to see Mrs Murgatroyd's companion set out on a shopping expedition. She was running to catch the bus.

Which meant she'd left the house in a hurry.

On an impulse, he slipped up the path and went around the side of the house. Oh, Mrs Murgatroyd saw him, of course. Propped in the window, as usual, her little black eyes missing nothing that went on in the neighbourhood. She was agitated, she bobbed about frantically, she even called out for help – but there was no one to hear her, now.

No one to tell, now.

He'd been right. The companion had left the back door ajar. Just a bit. Just enought. He was in like a shadow – he was good at that – and savoured the moment.

Mrs Murgatroyd, you've poked your nosy little beak into a neighbour's business just once too often, he thought to

himself. Now you'll find out just what I do, and how I do it.

Slowly, quietly, he moved across the kitchen and pushed open the door into the hall. The house smelled very different from his own. All houses had a characteristic smell, he was a connoisseur of smells, assigned personalities to houses on the basis of smells, knew what to expect the minute he was through a door. Some smelled richly of buttery meals and cream teas, some smelled rankly of cabbage and disinfectant. All of them smelled of death, after he'd dropped by.

This one would, too.

Moving stealthily, he slipped down the hall, his footsteps hardly making a whisper on the thick pile of the carpet. There – the sitting-room door was open, and he could hear Mrs Murgatroyd muttering to herself, alone in the room. She was talking about him. Words like 'murderer' and 'monster' rose above her inane jabbering.

He went in and she stopped her talk.

Gaped at him.

Moved back, as far back as she could.

She knew what he had come for, all right.

For all the good it would do her.

He thought it would be easy, but it wasn't. She *could* move, after all. She fled from him, darting around the room, then making a frantic, scrabbling dash for the hall, screeching and flailing and jabbering.

But he got her.

And it was good, so good. She twisted and turned and struggled but he got her, he finished her, and she would stare no more, jabber no more. Nasty, vicious, nosy little bag of bones.

Goodbye, Mrs Murgatroyd.

Now all he had to do was get out.

But luck wasn't with him.

Not this time.

The back door slammed – the companion was back! Too soon, too soon! Now she was in the doorway! Standing, staring, pointing at the scatter of green and blue on the carpet, and screaming!

Why did they all scream? Why were they so shocked?

What did they expect?

No other self-respecting cat would have put up with that damned budgie staring and screeching at him for another single day. Why should he?

He sighed and crawled under an armchair.

There'd be no pink salmon tonight.

FOCUS QUESTIONS

1   For most of the story, we are led to believe that the main character is human. Give three examples of words or sentences that give the cat human characteristics.

2   There are some early indications that 'He' is a cat, such as 'Everybody thought he was so quiet, so polite.' List two other sentences that describe cat-like characteristics.

3   Who is 'Dol'?

4   Now that you know what happens at the end of the story, explain the meaning of the following sentences.
    a   'After all, she was a shut-in, that was clear.'
    b   'Most of what she said was pure nonsense.'

5   What is 'The Business' that 'He' does?

6   Who is Mrs Murgatroyd?

7   In the story, the expression 'swell the kitty' has a double meaning.
    a   What does it usually mean?
    b   What does it mean in the context of this story?

8   Do you think the story's title is a good one? Explain your answer.

EXPLORING WORDS

9   Explain the meaning of the underlined words in the following extracts from the story.
    a   'And all the time she was complaining and crabbing.'
    b   'It made him cringe every time he passed by.'
    c   '. . . and savoured the moment.'
    d   '. . . some smelled rankly of cabbage and disinfectant.'
    e   'Moving stealthily, he slipped down the hall.'
    f   'Words like "murderer" and "monster" rose above her inane jabbering.'

WRITING

10 Write a story of your own in which an animal is portrayed as a human being. Try to include some of the typical characteristics of that animal, without giving away that it is an animal. Some possibilities are:

▶ A snake that lives in the hills and longs for a quiet life.

▶ An owl that is always out at night and disturbing the neighbours.

▶ A dog that is noisy and boisterous in the family home.

Yellow Belly

It was one of those quick, fierce storms, right overhead, that seemed about to split the house in two. There was a scratching and whining at the back door, then the latch gave way, and a great, yellow dog burst into the room.

He was drenched, and mud slicked the hair to his belly and legs. His big ugly head weaved from side to side as he scrabbled on the lino. As the thunder cracked over the house again, he let out a howl, and slid through Pa's legs and under the table. There he sat, shivering and cowering, as if all the demons in hell were after him.

Pa wasn't pleased about dogs under the kitchen table, especially wet dogs that rubbed mud all over his clean Sunday trousers. He put his head under the table and yelled at the dog to get his big yellow frame out of that back door or there'd be something coming to him. The dog whined and wriggled hard up against the wall.

So Pa crawled under the table and dragged the dog out by his back legs.

By this time, Ma was shouting that you couldn't put even a dog out on a night like this, I was howling, and the dog sounded as if he was being murdered.

Poor Pa. The odds were against him. He managed to drag

the dog as far as the door, but the dog did a crafty back-flip and slithered through Pa's legs again. Pa was up-ended on the lino, and the dog was safely back under the table.

Pa was wet, muddy, and madder than a hatful of wasps. He stamped off to bed, muttering that dogs were yellow bellies as well, they needed a bullet through their heads.

Yellow Belly settled in quite suddenly after that. One minute he was shivering under the table, the next minute the storm was over, and he was playing to Ma for something to eat, and thumping his tail as if he'd known us all our lives. Ma was putty-soft when it came to animals. She gave Yellow Belly a large bowl of left-over stew, then with my help she dunked him in the high old wooden bath tub in the outside washhouse and scrubbed him down.

From that night on, Yellow Belly seemed to regard us as his owners – except for Pa, that is.

At first Ma was concerned about her big flock of turkeys. Many local dogs regarded the turkeys as walking dinners. But Yellow Belly was quite docile as he followed her around on

her chores for the flock. He had a mouth as soft as silk. He could pick up a turkey chick in his jaws and carry it to Ma without making a mark on it.

He was scared, though. At the slightest sound out of the ordinary, he hared for the hedge and sat beneath it, cringing and whining. Even the farm cats lorded it over Yellow Belly. They ate his meat, drank his milk – one even shared his kennel.

'Call that a dog!' scoffed Pa. 'Fancy any self-respecting animal letting himself be bossed by a tribe of cats.' He gave Yellow Belly a nasty look out of the kitchen window. 'If we'd had any sense, we'd have got rid of that free-loader months ago.'

Ma just smiled, and dished Pa out another piece of his favourite apple pie. She knew Pa's bark was worse than his bite. But to Yellow Belly, Pa was the most frightening thing on the farm. Perhaps it was because Pa was a big, gruff man, with a loud voice and a quick way of moving. Perhaps it was because of the fright he'd had the night of the storm. Whatever it was, Yellow Belly became even more cowardly when Pa was around. He showed the whites of his eyes, lowered his head, and slunk off sideways, his hindquarters low to the ground; and if Pa made a move towards him, he'd let out little yelps of fear.

The Colonel called one day to order a turkey from Ma for Christmas dinner. He was a tall, silent, strange man who lived alone on an isolated little farm at the top of the valley. He came into the Takaka township every now and then to stock up his cupboards and get fresh ammunition for his guns. The Colonel was a hunting man and always had several dogs trotting obediently behind him.

Ma had just written down the order for the turkey when the Colonel saw Yellow Belly skulking past the back door. The man jumped off his chair, went red in the face, and asked Ma, in a shaking voice, what did she mean by stealing his dog. Ma was not to be bullied by the Colonel. She attacked right back.

'That dog was in a terrible state when he arrived here,' she said. 'We advertised him in the local paper. Why didn't you claim your dog then?'

The Colonel sat down again, apologised, and mumbled that he never really had time to read the papers.

Ma nodded and said it was time everyone had a cup of tea and talked it over. After a while Pa arrived on the scene, and pretty soon the Colonel had convinced everyone that Yellow Belly was his expensive pedigree gun dog, and that he thought the animal had drowned in the flooded Takaka River, several months before.

Then the Colonel got out a collar and chain from his car and started whistling to Yellow Belly. The big dog cowered and whined, and wouldn't let anyone touch him except Ma. Eventually she had to put the collar and chain on him and lift him into the car.

I think we all felt sad when the old car chugged out of the gate that day, even Pa, who said gruffly that perhaps Yellow Belly hadn't been a bad sort of dog in his way, and that he hoped that the Colonel would treat him properly.

We probably would never have seen Yellow Belly again if Pa hadn't had to deliver the turkey the following week. He took me with him, and we jogged over the narrow guttered road in our old Vauxhall, past hedges of gorse and hawthorn, right to the end of the valley where the Colonel lived. As we jarred over the Colonel's cattle stop, we could hear the sound of shooting in the distance.

'Must be getting in a bit of target practice,' said Pa, and he steered the car carefully over the rocky track leading up to the Colonel's house.

I was looking forward to seeing Yellow Belly again. I'd missed the big, gentle dog. I raced ahead of Pa, squeezing through the fence that surrounded the Colonel's little cottage. The shooting was echoing down the valley from somewhere behind the house and I slowed down until I could see exactly where the firing was coming from.

It took me a second or two to see the Colonel and the dog. Yellow Belly was tied to a stake in front of a large oak tree. He was lying in the dust and, even from where I stood, I could see the taut chain and the saliva frothing wet on his muzzle. Each shot the Colonel fired raised a puff of dust near the dog. 'Stand up, you cowardly mongrel!' he was shouting. 'Stand up and act like a gun dog! By crikey, I'm going to teach you some courage one day, or I'll put one of these bullets right through your yellow head!' The man's veins were standing out rope-like on his heavy red head. He looked mad enough to burst.

After every shot, Yellow Belly howled and rolled helplessly, his feet pawing the air.

Suddenly Pa was there, waving and shouting at the Colonel. The Colonel wasn't listening. He was firing, shouting, firing again, and the dog was howling. Each time the bullet pinged on the ground closer to the animal's head.

Pa ran towards the dog. He slid to the ground by the animal and slipped the collar off his big yellow head, fondling him gently. Yellow Belly whimpered and crawled close, licking Pa's hand.

The Colonel was silent with surprise. Then, as Pa stood up, the dog at his heels, he came running over, yelling that Pa had better get off his land or he'd get the same medicine as the dog.

Pa just shrugged his shoulders and turned his back to walk away, calling out that he was taking the dog home where he'd be looked after properly.

Suddenly the gun went off. The bullet flicked the dust by Pa's gumboot. Pa stood frozen to the spot, staring at the puff of dust. I think he was more amazed than frightened.

Then there was a flash of yellow. The dog flew through the air and onto the Colonel, growling and barking like a fury. The Colonel toppled under the weight of the animal. The two of them scrabbled in the dust, over and over, a blur of man and dog. Yellow Belly ended up astride the Colonel's chest, his teeth bared at the man's throat.

Pa had a hard time trying to get that dog off the Colonel. There was pulling and barking with the three of them scrambling in the dust. The Colonel acted as scared as Yellow Belly had

ever been. Pa could keep the mangey, flea-bitten cur, said the Colonel, and good riddance to him.

Pa told me later that the dog had probably run off in the first place because of the Colonel's ill-treatment of him. The moment we left the Colonel's farm, Yellow Belly became his old, gentle self again – or nearly. He was never really as frightened again. It was almost as if he had reached the bottom of his fear that day – had been as far down as he could go.

Pa became firm friends with Yellow Belly. As he said, it was hard to dislike a dog that had tried to save your life.

FOCUS QUESTIONS

1 How do Pa and Ma react to the dog's arrival at their house?

2 Explain the meaning of the following sentences.
   a 'Poor Pa. The odds were against him.'
   b 'Ma was putty-soft when it came to animals.'

3 Why is Ma concerned about her flock of turkeys?

4 Why does Pa call the dog 'Yellow Belly'?

5 What does Pa mean when he describes Yellow Belly as a 'free-loader'?

6 What was your first impression of the Colonel?

7 Why is the family sad to see Yellow Belly being taken away?

8 Why does the Colonel fire shots to raise the dust near Yellow Belly's head?

9 What is your opinion of the Colonel in the light of his behaviour and what he says to Pa?

10 Explain the ways in which the story's title is appropriate.

EXPLORING WORDS

11 Explain the meaning of the underlined words in the following extracts from the story.
   a 'There he sat, shivering and <u>cowering</u>.'
   b '. . . she <u>dunked</u> him in the high old wooden bath tub.'
   c 'But Yellow Belly was quite <u>docile</u> as he followed her around on her <u>chores</u> for the flock.'
   d '"Call that a dog!" <u>scoffed</u> Pa.'

DISCUSSION

12 'You couldn't put even a dog out on a night like this'. Ma uses a common saying to describe the weather. Discuss what the following sayings mean.
   a Every dog has its day.
   b Let sleeping dogs lie.
   c Once bitten, twice shy.

The Cyclops' Cave

After he had rescued his crew from Lotusland, Ulysses found that he was running from one trouble into another. They were still at sea, and there was no food for the fleet. The men were hungry and getting dangerous. Ulysses heard them grumbling: 'He should have left us there in Lotusland. At least when you're asleep you don't know you're hungry. Why did he have to come and wake us up?' He knew that unless he found food for them very soon he would be facing a mutiny.

That part of the Aegean Sea was dotted with islands. On every one of them was a different kind of enemy. The last thing Ulysses wanted to do was to go ashore, but there was no other way of getting food. He made a landfall on a small mountainous island. He was very careful; he had the ships of the fleet moor offshore and selected twelve of his bravest men as a landing party.

They beached their skiff and struck inland. It was a wild hilly place, full of boulders, with very few trees. It seemed deserted. Then Ulysses glimpsed something moving across the valley, on the slope of a hill. He was too far off to see what they were, but he thought they must be goats since the hill was so steep. And if they were goats they had to be caught. So the men headed downhill, meaning to cross the valley and climb the slope.

Ulysses had no way of knowing it, but this was the very worst island in the entire sea on which the small party could have landed. For here lived the Cyclopes, huge savage creatures, tall as trees, each with one eye in the middle of his forehead. Once, long ago, they had lived in the bowels of Olympus, forging thunderbolts for Zeus. But he had punished them for some fault, exiling them to this island where they had forgotten all their smithcraft and did nothing but fight with each other for the herds of wild goats, trying to find enough food to fill their huge bellies. Best of all, they liked storms; storms meant shipwrecks. Shipwrecks meant sailors struggling in the sea, who could be plucked out and eaten raw; and the thing they loved best in the world was human flesh. The largest and the fiercest and the hungriest of all the Cyclopes on the island was one named Polyphemus. He kept constant vigil on his mountain, fair weather or foul. If he spotted a ship, and there was no storm to help, he would dive into the sea and swim underwater, coming up underneath the ship and overturning it. Then he would swim off with his pockets full of sailors.

On this day he could not believe his luck when he saw a boat actually landing on the beach, and thirteen meaty-looking sailors disembark, and begin to march towards his cave. But here they were, climbing out of the valley now, up the slope of the hill, right towards the cave. He realised they must be hunting his goats.

The door of the cave was an enormous slab of stone. He shoved this aside so that the cave stood invitingly open, casting a faint glow of firelight upon the dusk. Over the fire, on a great spit, eight goats were turning and roasting. The delicious savours of the cooking drifted from the cave. Polyphemus lay down behind a huge boulder and waited.

The men were halfway up the slope of the hill when they smelled the meat roasting. They broke into a run. Ulysses tried to restrain them, but they paid no heed – they were too hungry. They raced to the mouth of the cave and dashed in. Ulysses drew his sword and hurried after them. When he saw the huge fireplace and the eight goats spitted like sparrows, his heart sank because he knew that they had come into reach of something much larger than themselves. However, the men were giving no thought to anything but food; they flung themselves on the spit, and tore into the goat meat, smearing their hands and faces with sizzling fat, too hungry to feel pain as they crammed the hot meat into their mouths.

There was a loud rumbling sound; the cave darkened. Ulysses whirled around. He saw that the door had been closed. The far end of the cavern was too dark to see anything, but then – amazed, aghast – he saw what looked like a huge red lantern far above, coming closer. Then he saw the great shadow of a nose under it, and the gleam of teeth. He realised that the lantern was a great flaming eye. Then he saw the whole giant, tall as a tree, with huge fingers reaching out of the shadows, fingers bigger than baling hooks. They closed around two sailors and hauled them screaming into the air.

As Ulysses and his horrified men watched, the great hand bore the struggling little men to the giant's mouth. He ate them, still wriggling, the way a cat eats a grasshopper; he ate them clothes and all, growling over their raw bones.

The men had fallen to their knees and were whimpering like terrified children, but Ulysses stood there, sword in hand, his agile brain working more swiftly than it ever had before.

'Greetings,' he called. 'May I know to whom we are indebted for such hospitality?'

The giant belched and spat out buttons. 'I am Polyphemus,' he growled. 'This is my cave, my mountain, and everything that comes here is mine. I do hope you can all stay to dinner. There are just enough of you to make a meal. Ho, ho . . .' And he laughed a great, choking phlegmy laugh, swiftly lunged, and caught another sailor, whom he lifted into the air and held before his face.

'Wait!' cried Ulysses.

'What for?'

'You won't enjoy him that way. He is from Attica, where the olives grow. He was raised on olives and has a very delicate oily flavour. But to appreciate it, you must taste the wine of the country.'

'Wine? What is wine?'

'It is a drink. Made from pressed grapes. Have you never drunk it?'

'We drink nothing but ox blood and buttermilk here.'

'Ah, you do not know what you have missed, gentle Polyphemus. Meat-eaters, in particular, love wine. Here, try it for yourself.'

Ulysses unslung from his belt a full flask of unwatered wine. He gave it to the giant, who put it to his lips and gulped. He coughed violently, and stuck the sailor in a little niche high up in the cave wall, then leaned his great slab of a face towards Ulysses and said:

'What did you say this drink was?'

'Wine. A gift of the gods to man, to make women look better and food taste better. And now it is my gift to you.'

'It's good, very good.' He put the bottle to his lips and swallowed again. 'You are very polite. What's your name?'

'My name? Why I am – nobody.'

'Nobody . . . Well, Nobody, I like you. You're a good fellow. And do you know what I'm going to do? I'm going to save you till last. Yes, I'll eat all your friends first, and give you extra time, that's what I'm going to do.'

Ulysses looked up into the great eye and saw that it was redder than ever. It was all a swimming redness. He had given the monster, who had never drunk spirits before, undiluted wine. Surely it must make him sleepy. But was a gallon enough for that great gullet? Enough to put him to sleep – or would he want to eat again first?

'Eat 'em all up, Nobody – save you till later. Sleep a little first. Shall I? Won't try to run away, will you? No – you can't, can't open the door – too heavy, ha, ha . . . You take a nap too, Nobody. I'll wake you for breakfast. Breakfast . . .'

The great body crashed full-length on the cave floor, making the very walls of the mountain shake. Polyphemus lay on his back, snoring like a powersaw. The sailors were still on the floor, almost dead from fear.

'Up!' cried Ulysses. 'Stand up like men! Do what must be done! Or you will be devoured like chickens.'

He got them to their feet and drew them about him as he explained his plan.

'Listen now, and listen well, for we have no time. I made him drunk, but we cannot tell how long it will last.'

Ulysses thrust his sword into the fire; they saw it glow white-hot.

'There are ten of us,' he said. 'Two of us have been eaten, and one of our friends is still unconscious up there on his shelf of rock. You four get on one side of his head, and the rest on the other side. When I give the word, lay hold of the ear on your side, each of you. And hang on, no matter how he thrashes, for I am going to put out his eye. And if I am to be sure of my stroke you must hold his head still. One stroke is all I will be allowed.'

Then Ulysses rolled a boulder next to the giant's head and climbed on it, so that he was looking down into the eye. It was lidless and misted with sleep – big as a furnace door and glowing softly like a banked fire. Ulysses looked at his men. They had done what he said, broken into two parties, one group at each ear. He lifted his white-hot sword.

'Now!' he cried.

Driving down with both hands, and all the strength of his back and shoulders, and all his rage and all his fear, Ulysses stabbed the glowing spike into the giant's eye.

His sword jerked out of his hand as the head flailed upward, men pelted to the ground as they lost their hold. A huge screeching curdling bellow split the air.

'This way!' shouted Ulysses.

He motioned to his men, and they crawled on their bellies towards the far end of the cave where the herd of goats was tethered. They slipped into the herd and lay among the goats as the giant stomped about the cave, slapping the walls with great blows of his hands, picking up boulders and cracking them together in agony, splitting them to flinders, clutching his eye, a scorched hole now from which the brown blood jelled. He moaned and gibbered and bellowed in frightful pain; his groping hand found the sailor in the wall, and he tore him to pieces between his fingers. Ulysses could not even hear the man scream because the giant was bellowing so.

Now Ulysses saw that the Cyclops' wild stampeding was giving place to a plan. For now he was stamping on the floor in a regular pattern, trying to find and crush them beneath his feet. He stopped moaning and listened. The sudden silence dazed the men with fear. They held their breath and tried to muffle the sound of their beating hearts; all the giant heard was the breathing of the goats. Then Ulysses saw him go to the mouth of the cave, and swing the great slab aside, and stand there. He realised just in time that the goats would rush outside, which is what the giant wanted, for then he could search the whole cave.

Ulysses whispered: 'Quickly, swing under the bellies of the rams. Hurry, hurry!'

Luckily, they were giant goats and thus able to carry the men who had swung themselves under their bellies and were clinging to the wiry wool. Ulysses himself chose the largest ram. They moved towards the mouth of the cave, and crowded through. The Cyclops' hands came down and brushed across the goats' backs feeling for the men, but the animals were huddled too closely together for him to reach between and search under their bellies. So he let them pass through.

Now, the Cyclops rushed to the corner where the goats had been tethered, and stamped, searched, and roared through the whole cave again, bellowing with fury when he did not find them. The herd grazed on the slope of the hill beneath the cave. There was a full moon; it was almost as bright as day.

'Stay where you are,' Ulysses whispered.

He heard a crashing, peered out, and saw great shadowy figures converging on the cave. He knew that the other Cyclopes

of the island must have heard the noise, and come to see. He heard the giant bellow.

The others called to him: 'Who has done it? Who has blinded you?'

'Nobody. Nobody did it. Nobody blinded me.'

'Ah, you have done it yourself. What a tragic accident.'

And they went back to their own caves.

'Now!' said Ulysses. 'Follow me!'

He swung himself out from under the belly of the ram, and raced down the hill. The others raced after him. They were halfway across the valley when they heard great footsteps rushing after them, and Polyphemus bellowing nearer and nearer.

'He's coming!' cried Ulysses. 'Run for your lives!'

They ran as they had never run before, but the giant could cover fifty yards at a stride. It was only because he could not see and kept bumping into trees and rocks that they were able to reach the skiff and push out on the silver water before Polyphemus burst out of the grove of trees and rushed onto the beach. They bent to the oars, and the boat scudded towards the fleet.

Polyphemus heard the dip of the oars and the groaning of the oarlocks, and, aiming at the sound, hurled huge boulders after them. They fell all around the ship, but did not hit. The skiff reached Ulysses' ship, and the sailors climbed aboard.

'Haul anchor, and away!' cried Ulysses. And then called to the Cyclops: 'Poor fool! Poor blinded drunken gluttonous fool – if anyone else asks you, it is not Nobody, but Ulysses who has done this to you.'

But he was to regret this final taunt. The gods honour courage, but punish pride.

Polyphemus, wild with rage, waded out chest-deep and hurled a last boulder, which hit mid-deck, almost sunk the ship, and killed most of the crew – among them seven of the nine men who had just escaped.

And Polyphemus prayed to Poseidon: 'God of the Sea, I beg you, punish Ulysses for this. Visit him with storm and shipwreck and sorceries. Let him wander many years before he reaches home, and when he gets there let him find himself forgotten, unwanted, a stranger.'

Poseidon heard this prayer, and made it all happen just that way.

FOCUS QUESTIONS

1 Why does Ulysses believe that his men are close to mutiny?

2 In which waters is Ulysses sailing?

3 Why does Ulysses want to go ashore?

4 Why do the Cyclopes enjoy storms?

5 **a** Who is Polyphemus?
 b How does he lure Ulysses' men into his cave?

6 How does Ulysses persuade Polyphemus not to eat the sailor from Attica?

7 Why does Polyphemus decide to wait a while before he eats Ulysses and the rest of the sailors?

8 Explain the meaning of the following extract: 'Now Ulysses saw that the Cyclops' wild stampeding was giving place to a plan.'

9 What makes the other Cyclopes believe that Polyphemus had accidentally blinded himself?

10 Explain the meaning of the following sentence: 'But he [Ulysses] was to regret this final taunt.'

EXPLORING WORDS

11 The following extracts from the story are missing punctuation. Insert the punctuation in the sentences and then check the original story.
 a greetings he called may i know to whom we are indebted for such hospitality
 the giant belched and spat out buttons i am polyphemus he growled this is my cave my mountain and everything that comes here is mine i do hope you can all stay to dinner
 b what did you say this drink was
 wine a gift of the gods to man to make women look better and food taste better and now it is my gift to you

its good very good he put the bottle to his lips and swallowed again you are very polite whats your name

my name why i am – nobody

nobody . . . well nobody i like you youre a good fellow and do you know what im going to do im going to save you till last yes ill eat all your friends first and give you extra time thats what im going to do

WRITING

12 Write five sentences about 'The Cyclops' Cave', using as many of the following words from the story as you can. (The words have been grouped under different headings to make it easier for you.)

Nouns	Verbs	Adjectives
Agony	Bellowed	Aghast
Hospitality	Crashed	Dangerous
Mutiny	Dashed	Delicate
Taunt	Devoured	Enormous
Vigil	Flailed	Fiercest
	Gibbered	Foul
	Horrified	Largest
	Moaned	Raw
	Pelted	Unconscious
	Stamped	Undiluted

Three Skeleton Key

My most terrifying experience? Well, one does have a few in thirty-five years of service in the Lights, although it's mostly monotonous routine work – keeping the light in order, making out the reports.

When I was a young man, not very long in the service, there was an opening in a lighthouse newly built off the coast of Guiana, on a small rock twenty miles or so from the mainland. The pay was high, so in order to reach the sum I had set out to save before I married, I volunteered for service in the new light.

Three Skeleton Key, the small rock on which the light stood, bore a bad reputation. It earned its name from the story of the three convicts who, escaping from Cayenne in a stolen dugout canoe, were wrecked on the rock during the night, managed to escape the sea but eventually died of hunger and thirst. When they were discovered, nothing remained but three heaps of bones, picked clean by the birds. The story was that the three skeletons gleaming with phosphorescent light, danced over the small rock, screaming . . .

But there are many such stories and I did not give the warnings of the old-timers at the *Isle de Sein* a second thought. I signed up, boarded ship and in a month I was installed at the light.

Picture a grey, tapering cylinder, welded to the solid black rock by iron rods and concrete, rising from a small island twenty odd miles from land. It lay in the midst of the sea, this island, a small, bare piece of stone, about one hundred and fifty feet long, perhaps forty, wide. Small, barely large enough for a man to walk about and stretch his legs at low tide.

This is an advantage one doesn't find in all lights, however, for some of them rise sheer from the waves, with no room for one to move save within the light itself. Still, on our island, one must be careful, for the rocks were treacherously smooth. One misstep and down you would fall into the sea – not that the risk of drowning was so great, but the waters about our island swarmed with huge sharks who kept an eternal patrol around the base of the light.

Still, it was a nice life there. We had enough provisions to last for months, in the event that the sea should become too rough for the supply ship to reach us on schedule. During the day we would work about the light, cleaning the rooms, polishing the metalwork and the lens and reflector of the light itself, and at night we would sit on the gallery and watch our light, a twenty thousand candle-power lantern, swinging its strong, white bar of light over the sea from the top of its hundred and twenty foot tower. Some days, when the air would be very clear, we could see the land, a thread-like line to the west. To the east, north and south stretched the ocean. Landsmen, perhaps, would soon have tired of that kind of life, perched on a small island off the coast of South America for eighteen weeks, until one's turn for leave ashore came around. But we liked it there, my two fellow-tenders and myself – so much so that, for twenty-two months on end with the exception of shore leaves, I was greatly satisfied with the life on Three Skeleton Key.

I had just returned from my leave at the end of June, that is to say mid-winter in that latitude, and had settled down to the routine with my two fellow-keepers, a Breton by the name of Le Gleo and the head-keeper, Itchoua, a Basque some dozen years or so older than either of us.

Eight days went by as usual, then on the ninth after my return, Itchoua, who was on night duty, called Le Gleo and me, sleeping in our rooms in the middle of the tower, at two in the morning. We rose immediately and, climbing the thirty or so steps that led to the gallery, stood beside our chief.

Itchoua pointed, and following his finger, we saw a big three-master, with all sail set, heading straight for the light. A queer course, for the vessel must have seen us, our light lit her with the glare of day each time it passed over her.

Now, ships were a rare sight in our waters, for our light was a warning of treacherous reefs, barely hidden under the surface and running far out to sea. Consequently we were always given a wide berth, especially by sailing vessels, which cannot manoeuvre as readily as steamers.

No wonder that we were surprised at seeing this three-master heading dead for us in the gloom of early morning. I had immediately recognised her lines, for she stood out plainly, even at the distance of a mile, when our light shone on her.

She was a beautiful ship of some four thousand tons, a fast sailer that had carried cargoes to every part of the world, ploughing the seas unceasingly. By her lines she was identified as Dutch-built, which was understandable as Paramaribo and Dutch Guiana are very close to Cayenne.

Watching her sailing dead for us, a white wave boiling under her bows, Le Gleo cried out:

'What's wrong with her crew? Are they all drunk or insane? Can't they see us?'

Itchoua nodded soberly, looked at us sharply as he remarked: 'See us? No doubt – if there *is* a crew aboard!'

'What do you mean, chief?' Le Gleo had started, turned to the Basque, 'Are you saying that she's the *Flying Dutchman*?'

His sudden fright had been so evident that the older man laughed:

'No, old man, that's not what I meant. If I say that no one's aboard, I mean she's a derelict.'

Then we understood her queer behaviour. Itchoua was right. For some reason, believing her doomed, her crew had abandoned her. Then she had righted herself and sailed on, wandering with the wind.

The three of us grew tense as the ship seemed about to crash on one of our numerous reefs, but she suddenly lurched with some change of the wind, the yards swung around and the derelict came clumsily about and sailed dead away from us.

In the light of our lantern she seemed so sound, so strong, that Itchoua exclaimed impatiently:

'But why the devil was she abandoned? Nothing is smashed, no sign of fire – and she doesn't sail as if she were taking water.'

Le Gleo waved to the departing ship:

'*Bon voyage!*' he smiled at Itchoua and went on, 'She's leaving us, chief, and now we'll never know what . . .

'No she's not!' cried the Basque. 'Look! She's turning!'

As if obeying his words, the derelict three-master stopped, came about and headed for us once more. And for the next four hours the vessel played around us – zigzagging, coming about, stopping, then suddenly lurching forward. No doubt some freak of current and wind, of which our island was the centre, kept her near us.

Then suddenly the tropic dawn broke, the sun rose and it was day and the ship was plainly visible as she sailed past us. Our light extinguished, we returned to the gallery with our glasses and inspected her.

The three of us focused our glasses on her poop, saw standing our sharply, black letters on the white background of a life-ring, the stencilled name:

'*Cornelius de Witt, Rotterdam*.'

We had read her lines correctly, she was Dutch. Just then the wind rose and the *Cornelius de Witt* changed course, leaned to port and headed straight for us once more. But this time she was so close that we knew she would not turn in time.

'Thunder!' cried Le Gleo, his Breton soul aching to see a fine ship doomed to smash upon a reef, 'she's going to pile up! She's gone!'

I shook my head:

'Yes, and a shame to see that beautiful ship wreck herself. And we're helpless.'

There was nothing we could do but watch. A ship sailing with all sail spread, creaming the sea with her forefoot as she runs before the wind, is one of the most beautiful sights in the world – but this time I could feel the tears stinging in my eyes as I saw this fine ship headed for her doom.

All this time our glasses were riveted on her and we suddenly cried out together:

'The rats!'

Now we knew why this ship, in perfect condition, was sailing without her crew aboard. They had been driven out by the rats. Not those poor specimens of rats you see ashore, barely reaching the length of one foot from their trembling noses to the tip of their skinny tails, wretched creatures that dodge and hide at the mere sound of a footfall.

No, these were ship's rats, huge, wise creatures, born on the sea, sailing all over the world on ships, transferring to other, larger ships as they multiply. There is as much difference between the rats of the land and these maritime rats as between a fishing smack and an armoured cruiser.

The rats of the sea are fierce, bold animals. Large, strong and intelligent, clannish and seawise, able to put the best of mariners to shame with their knowledge of the sea, their uncanny ability to foretell the weather.

And they are brave, these rats, and vengeful. If you so much as harm one, his sharp cry will bring hordes of his fellows to swarm over you, tear you and not cease until your flesh has been stripped from the bones.

The ones on this ship, the rats of Holland, are the worst, superior to other rats of the sea as their brethren are to the land rats. There is a well-known tale about these animals.

A Dutch captain, thinking to protect his cargo, brought aboard his ship – not cats – but two terriers, dogs trained in the hunting, fighting and killing of vicious rats. By the time the ship, sailing from Rotterdam, had passed the Ostend light, the dogs were gone and never seen again. In twenty-four hours they had been overwhelmed, killed and eaten by the rats.

At times, when the cargo does not suffice, the rats attack the crew, either driving them from the ship or eating them alive. And studying the *Cornelius de Witt*, I turned sick, for her small boats were all in place. She had not been abandoned.

Over her bridge, on her deck, in the rigging, on every visible spot, the ship was a writhing mass – a starving army coming towards us aboard a vessel gone mad!

Our island was a small spot in that immense stretch of sea. The ship could have grazed us, passed to port or starboard with its ravening cargo – but no, she came for us at full speed, as if she were leading the regatta at a race, and impaled herself on a sharp point of rock.

There was a dull shock as her bottom stove in, then a horrible crackling as the three masts went overboard at once, as if cut down with one blow of some gigantic sickle. A sighing groan came as the water rushed into the ship, then she split in two and sank like a stone.

But the rats did not drown. Not these fellows! As much at home in the sea as any fish, they formed ranks in the water, heads lifted, tails stretched out, paws paddling. And half of them, those from the forepart of the ship, sprang along the masts and on to the rocks in the instant before she sank. Before we had time to move, nothing remained of the three-master save some pieces of wreckage floating on the surface and an army of rats covering the rocks left bare by the receding tide.

Thousands of heads rose, felt the wind and we were scented, seen! To them we were fresh meat, after possible weeks of starving. There came a scream, composed of innumerable screams, sharper than the howl of a saw attacking a bar of iron, and in the one motion, every rat leaped to attack the tower!

We barely had time to leap back, close the door leading on to the gallery, descend the stairs and shut every window tightly. Luckily the door at the base of the light, which we

never could have reached in time, was of bronze set in granite and was tightly closed.

The horrible band, in no measurable time, had swarmed up and over the tower as if it had been a tree, piled on the embrasures of the windows, scraped at the glass with thousands of claws, covered the lighthouse with a furry mantle and reached the top of the tower, filling the gallery and piling atop the lantern.

Their teeth grated as they pressed against the glass of the lantern-room, where they could plainly see us, though they could not reach us. A few millimetres of glass, luckily very strong, separated our faces from their gleaming, beady eyes, their sharp claws and teeth. Their odour filled the tower, poisoned our lungs and rasped our nostrils with a pestilential, nauseating smell. And there we were, sealed alive in our own light, prisoners of a horde of starving rats.

That first night the tension was so great that we could not sleep. Every moment we felt that some opening had been made, some window given away, and that our horrible besiegers were pouring through the breach. The rising tide, chasing those of the rats which had stayed on the bare rocks, increased the numbers clinging to the walls, piled on the balcony – so much so that clusters of rats clinging to one another hung from the lantern and the gallery.

With the coming of darkness we lit the light and the turning beam completely maddened the beasts. As the light turned, it successivly blinded thousands of rats crowded against the glass, while the dark side of the lantern-room gleamed with thousands of points of light, burning like the eyes of jungle beasts in the night.

All the while we could hear the enraged scraping of claws against the stone and glass, while the chorus of cries was so loud that we had to shout to hear one another. From time to time, some of the rats fought among themselves and a dark cluster would detach itself, falling into the sea like a ripe fruit from a tree. Then we would see phosphorescent streaks as tringular fins slashed the water – sharks, permanent guardians of our rock, feasting on our jailers.

The next day we were calmer, and amused ourselves teasing the rats, placing our faces against the glass which separated us. They could not fathom the invisible barrier which separated them from us and we laughed as we watched them leaping against the heavy glass.

But the day after that we realised how serious our position was. The air was foul, even the heavy smell of oils within our stronghold could not dominate the fetid odour of the beasts massed around us. And there was no way of admitting fresh air without also admitting the rats.

The morning of the fourth day, at early dawn, I saw the wooden framework of my window, eaten away from the outside, sagging inwards. I called my comrades and the three of us fastened a sheet of tin in the opening, sealing it tightly. When we had completed the task, Itchoua turned to us and said dully:

'Well – the supply boat came thirteen days ago, and she won't be back for twenty-nine.' He pointed at the white metal plate sealing the opening through the granite – 'if that gives way –' he shrugged – 'they can change the name of this place to Six Skeletons Key.'

The next six days and seven nights our only distraction was watching the rats whose holds were insecure fall a hundred and twenty feet into the maws of the sharks – but they were so many that we could not see any diminution in their numbers.

Thinking to calm ourselves and pass the time, we attempted to count them, but we soon gave up. They moved incessantly, never still. Then we tried identifying them, naming them.

One of them, larger than the others, who seemed to lead them in their rushes against the glass separating us, we named 'Nero'; and there were several others whom we had learned to distinguish through various peculiarities.

But the thought of our bones joining those of the convicts was always in the back of our minds. And the gloom of our prison fed these thoughts, for the interior of the light was almost completely dark, as we had to seal every window in the same fashion as mine, and the only space that still admitted daylight was the glassed-in lantern-room at the very top of the tower.

Then Le Gleo became morose and had nightmares in which he would see the three skeletons dancing around him, gleaming coldly, seeking to grasp him. His maniacal, raving descriptions were so vivid that Itchoua and I began seeing them also.

It was a living nightmare, the raging cries of the rats as they swarmed over the light, mad with hunger; the sickening, strangling odour of their bodies . . .

True, there is a way of signalling from lighthouses. But to reach the mast on which to hang the signal we would have to go out on the gallery where the rats were.

There was only one thing left to do. After debating all of the ninth day, we decided not to light the lantern that night. This is the greatest breach of our service, never committed as long as the tenders of the light are alive; for the light is something sacred, warning ships of danger in the night. Either the light gleams, a quarter hour after sundown, or no one is left alive to light it.

Well, that night, Three Skeleton Light was dark, and all the men were alive. At the risk of causing ships to crash on our reefs, we left it unlit, for we were worn out – going mad!

At two in the morning, while Itchoua was dozing in his room, the sheet of metal sealing his window gave way. The chief had just enough time to leap to his feet and cry for help, the rats swarming over him.

But Le Gleo and I, who had been watching from the lantern-room, got to him immediately, and the three of us battled with the horde of maddened rats which flowed through the gaping window. They bit, we struck them down with our knives – and retreated.

We locked the door of the room on them, but before we had time to bind our wounds, the door was eaten through, and gave way and we retreated up the stairs, fighting off the rats that leaped on us from the knee deep swarm.

I do not remember, to this day, how we ever managed to escape. All I can remember is wading through them up the stairs, striking them off as they swarmed over us; and then we found ourselves, bleeding from innumerable bites, our clothes shredded, sprawled across the trapdoor in the floor of the lantern-room – without food or drink. Luckily, the trapdoor was metal set into the granite with iron bolts.

The rats occupied the entire light beneath us, and on the floor of our retreat lay some twenty of their fellows, who had come in with us before the trapdoor closed, and whom we had killed with our knives. Below us, in the tower, we could hear the screams of the rats as they devoured everything edible that they found. Those on the outside squealed in reply, and writhed in a horrible curtain as they stared at us through the glass of the lantern-room.

Itchoua sat up, stared silently at his blood trickling from the wounds on his limbs and body, and running in thin streams on the floor around him. Le Gleo, who was in as bad a state (and so was I, for that matter) stared at the chief and me vacantly, started as his gaze swung to the multitude of rats against the glass, then suddenly began laughing horribly:

'Hee! Hee! The Three Skeletons! Hee! Hee! The Three Skeletons are now *six* skeletons! *Six* skeletons!'

He threw his head back and howled, his eyes glazed, a trickle of saliva running from the corners of his mouth and thinning the blood flowing over his chest. I shouted to him to shut up, but he did not hear me, so I did the only thing I could to quiet him – I swung the back of my hand across his face.

The howling stopped suddenly, his eyes swung around the room, then he bowed his head and began weeping softly, like a child.

Our darkened light had been noticed from the mainland, and as dawn was breaking the patrol was there, to investigate the failure of our light. Looking through my binoculars, I

could see the horrified expression on the faces of the officers and crew when, the daylight strengthening, they saw the light completely covered by a seething mass of rats. They thought, as I afterwards found out, that we had been eaten alive.

But the rats had also seen the ship, or had scented the crew. As the ship drew nearer, a solid phalanx left the light, plunged into the water and, swimming out, attempted to board her. They would have succeeded, as the ship was hove to, but the engineer connected his steam to a hose on the deck and scalded the head of the attacking column, which slowed them up long enough for the ship to get under way and leave the rats behind.

Then the sharks took part. Belly up, mouths gaping, they arrived in swarms and scooped up the rats, sweeping through them like a sickle through wheat. That was one day that sharks really served a useful purpose.

The remaining rats turned tail, swam to the shore and emerged dripping. As they neared the light, their comrades greeted them with shrill cries, with what sounded like a derisive note predominating. They answered angrily and mingled with their fellows. From the several tussles that broke out, they resented being ridiculed for the failure to capture the ship.

But all this did nothing to get us out of our jail. The small ship could not approach, but steamed around the light at a safe distance, and the tower must have seemed fantastic, some weird, many-mouthed beast hurling defiance at them.

Finally, seeing the rats running in and out of the tower through the door and the windows, those on the ship decided that we had perished and were about to leave when Itchoua, regaining his senses, thought of using the light as a signal. He lit it and, using a plank placed and withdrawn before the beam to form the dots and dashes, quickly sent out our story to those on the vessel.

Our reply came quickly. When they understood our position, how we could not get rid of the rats, Le Gleo's mind going fast, Itchoua and myself covered with bites, cornered in the lantern-room without food or water, they had a signal-man send us their reply.

His arms, swinging like those of a windmill, he quickly spelled out:

'Don't give up, hang on a little longer! We'll get you out of this!'

Then she turned and steamed at top speed for the coast, leaving us little reassured.

She was back at noon, accompanied by the supply ship, two small coast guard boats, and the fire boat – a small squadron. At twelve-thirty the battle was on.

After a short reconnaissance, the fire boat picked her way slowly through the reefs until she was close to us, then turned her powerful jet of water on the rats. The heavy stream tore the rats from their places, hurled them screaming into the water where the sharks gulped them down. But for every ten that were dislodged, seven swam ashore, and the stream could do nothing to the rats within the tower. Furthermore, some of them, instead of returning to the rocks, boarded the fire boat

and the men were forced to battle them hand to hand. They were true rats of Holland, fearing no man, fighting for the right to live!

Nightfall came, and it was as if nothing had been done, the rats were still in possession. One of the patrol boats stayed by the island, the rest of the flotilla departed for the coast. We had to spend another night in our prison. Le Gleo was sitting on the floor, babbling about skeletons and as I turned to Itchoua, he fell unconscious from his wounds. I was in no better shape and could feel my blood flaming with fever.

Somehow the night dragged by, and the next afternoon I saw a tug, accompanied by the fire boat, come from the mainland with a huge barge in tow. Through my glasses I saw that the barge was filled with meat.

Risking the treacherous reefs, the tug dragged the barge as close to the island as possible. To the last rat, our besiegers deserted the rock, swam out and boarded the barge reeking with the scent of freshly cut meat. The tug dragged the barge about a mile from shore, where the fire boat drenched the barge with gasoline. A well placed incendiary shell from the patrol boat set her on fire.

The barge was covered with flames immediately and the rats took to the water in swarms, but the patrol boat bombarded them with shrapnel from a safe distance, and the sharks finished off the survivors.

A whaleboat from the patrol boat took us off the island and left three men to replace us. By nightfall we were in the hospital in Cayenne. But what became of my friends?

Well, Le Gleo's mind had cracked and he was raving mad. They sent him back to France and locked him up in an asylum, the poor devil; Itchoua died within a week; a rat's bite is dangerous in that hot, humid climate, and infection sets in rapidly.

As for me – when they fumigated the light and repaired the damage done by the rats, I resumed my service there. Why not? No reason why such an incident should keep me from finishing out my service there, is there?

Besides – I told you I liked the place – to be truthful, I've never had a post as pleasant as that one, and when my time came to leave for ever, I tell you that I almost wept as Three Skeleton Key disappeared below the horizon.

FOCUS QUESTIONS

1 Why does the narrator choose to work at the lighthouse on Three Skeleton Key?

2 Why is the island named Three Skeleton Key?

3 What are some of the advantages and disadvantages of living on the island?

4 Why are ships rarely sighted in waters close to the lighthouse?

5 What is the *Flying Dutchman*?

6 Explain the meaning of the following sentence: 'We had read her lines correctly, she was Dutch.'

7 In what respects are the rats on the *Cornelius de Witt* different from other rats?

8 What is the main danger faced by the lighthouse-keepers, despite their apparent security within the lighthouse?

9 Why are the men determined, but reluctant, not to light the lantern on the ninth night?

10 Give a number of reasons why the members of the patrol boat couldn't come ashore to save the party on Three Skeleton Key.

EXPLORING WORDS

11 Match the underlined words from the story with their appropriate meanings in the second column.

Words from the story

a 'We had enough <u>provisions</u> to last for months.'
b '. . . the <u>gloom</u> of early morning.'
c '. . . will bring <u>hordes</u> of his fellows to swarm.'
d '. . . sweeping through them like a <u>sickle</u>.'
e '. . . many-mouthed beast hurling <u>defiance</u>.'
f 'After a short <u>reconnaissance</u>.'
g '. . . the rest of the <u>flotilla</u> departed.'
h '. . . bombarded them with <u>shrapnel</u>.'

Meanings

Open resistance.
Food supplies.
Darkness.
Large groups.
A short-handled tool with a curved blade.
A small fleet of ships.
A survey of enemy or unknown territory.
Fragments from an exploding shell.

WRITING

12 Imagine that you are a reporter who went to Three Skeleton
Key on the rescue boat. Write an account of your experiences
in a style suitable for a newspaper article.

FURTHER ACTIVITIES

13 Arrange an interview with the narrator in the story. Write
up a list of questions, asking him about his life and work.
Then select one person to be the narrator and the other
the interviewer.

14 Imagine that you are assigned to a term of duty on Three
Skeleton Key. Make a list of all the things you would take
with you and be prepared to explain your selection of items.
(You cannot take anything which you are unable to carry
on your own.)

Flannan Isle

'Though three men dwell on Flannan Isle,
To keep the lamp alight,
As we steered under the lee, we caught
No glimmer through the night.'

A passing ship at dawn had brought
The news, and quickly we set sail,
To find out what strange thing might ail
The keepers of the deep-sea light.

The winter day broke blue and bright
With glancing sun and glancing spray
While o'er the swell our boat made way,
As gallant as a gull in flight.

But as we neared the lonely Isle
And looked up at the naked height,
And saw the lighthouse towering white
With blinded lantern, that all night
Had never shot a spark
Of comfort through the dark,
So ghostly in the cold sunlight
It seemed that we were struck the while
With wonder all too dread for words.

And, as into the tiny creek
We stole beneath the hanging crag,
We saw three queer black ugly birds –
Too big by far in my belief,
For cormorant or shag –
Like seamen sitting bolt-upright
Up on a half-tide reef:
But, as we neared, they plunged from sight
Without a sound or spurt of white.

And still too mazed to speak,
We landed; and made fast the boat;
And climbed the track in single file,
Each wishing he was safe afloat
On any sea, however far,
So it be far from Flannan Isle:
And still we seemed to climb and climb
As though we'd lost all count of time,
And so must climb for evermore.
Yet, all too soon, we reached the door –
The black, sun-blistered lighthouse-door,
That gaped for us ajar.

As, on the threshold, for a spell
We paused, we seemed to breathe the smell
Of limewash and of tar,
Familiar as our daily breath,
As though 'twere some strange scent of death
And so yet wondering, side by side
We stood a moment still tongue-tied;
And each with black foreboding eyed
The door, ere we should fling it wide
To leave the sunlight for the gloom:
Till, plucking courage up, at last
Hard on each other's heels we passed
Into the living-room.

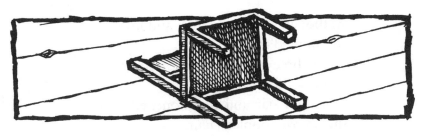

Yet, as we crowded through the door
We only saw a table, spread
For dinner, meat and cheese and bread;
But all untouched; and no one there:
As though, when they sat down to eat,
Ere they could even taste,
Alarm had come; and they in haste
Had risen and left the bread and meat,
For at the table-head a chair
Lay tumbled on the floor.

We listened, but we only heard
The feeble chirping of a bird
That starved upon its perch;
And, listening still, without a word
We set about our hopeless search.
We hunted high, we hunted low,
And soon ransacked the empty house;

Then o'er the Island, to and fro
We ranged, to listen and to look
In every cranny, cleft or nook
That might have hid a bird or mouse:

But though we searched from shore to shore
We found no sign in any place,
And soon again stood face to face
Before the gaping door,
And stole into the room once more
As frightened children steal.

Ay, though we hunted high and low
And hunted everywhere,
Of the three men's fate we found no trace
Of any kind in any place
But a door ajar, and an untouched meal,
And an overtoppled chair.

And as we listened in the gloom
Of that forsaken living-room –
A chill clutch on our breath –
We thought how ill-chance came to all
Who kept the Flannan Light,
And how the rock had been the death
Of many a likely lad –
How six had come to a sudden end
And three had gone stark mad,
And one whom we'd all known as friend,
Had leapt from the lantern one still night,
And fallen dead by the lighthouse wall –
And long we thought
On the three we sought,
And on what might yet befall.

Like curs a glance has brought to heel
We listened, flinching there,
And looked, and looked, on the untouched meal,
And the overtoppled chair.

We seemed to stand for an endless while,
Though still no word was said,
Three men alive on Flannan Isle
Who thought on three men dead.

FOCUS QUESTIONS

1   Who first reported that the light on the Isle had gone out?

2   During which season of the year do the events described in the poem take place?

3   What leads the narrator to believe that the three birds are neither cormorants nor shags?

4   Why does the party approach the lighthouse in silence?

5   Why is everybody reluctant to go inside the lighthouse?

6   What evidence is there to indicate that the previous lighthouse keepers had left in a hurry?

7   List the number of ways in which 'ill-chance' (bad luck) had come to the other people who had lived on Flannan Isle.

8   Apart from 'black' and 'white', there are no other colours mentioned in this narrative. Can you think of any reasons why this might be?

EXPLORING WORDS

9   Explain the meaning of the following phrases from the story, paying particular attention to the underlined words.
   a   '. . . our boat made way, / As gallant as a gull in flight.'
   b   'The black, sun-blistered lighthouse-door, / That gaped for us ajar.'
   c   'And each with black foreboding eyed / The door.'
   d   'We hunted high, we hunted low, / And soon ransacked the empty house.'

WRITING

10 This narrative poem is actually based on a true report received on 26 December 1900 – that the lighthouse on Flannan Isle had gone out. Imagine that you are a reporter who went to Flannan Isle with the search party. Write an account of your experiences in a style suitable for either a television program or news story, or a newspaper article.

A Tinned World

he Zerbini family, having picnicked on the slopes of the Tolfa Mountains, were getting ready to go back to Rome. Signor Zerbini was a nature lover. He was also very neat, and he told the remaining Zerbinis – Octavia his wife, his two sons Angelo and Piero, his daughter Rosella and her fiancé Pierrluigi – not to leave any pieces of paper or rubbish around.

'Let's do it properly,' he said. 'Not in a pile as you usually do. Look, this bush doesn't even have one paper cup in it. Now, make sure every tree plays its part – no favouritism please. Throw that dirty table cloth under this oak tree, and what about putting the empty bottles under that chestnut tree? There, doesn't that look better?'

There were three empty bottles: one beer bottle, one orangeade bottle and a mineral water bottle. They made a charming tableau at the foot of the chestnut tree. Angelo and Piero wanted to use them as a target for throwing stones but there wasn't enough time. They jumped into the car, said goodbye to the trees and with much merry hooting departed for Rome.

On they drove. When they were halfway down Allumiere mountain Angelo and Piero, who had been looking out of the back window and making faces at the drivers in the cars behind suddenly noticed that the empty beer bottle they had left under the tree had not been left behind at all. It was trotting briskly behind the car on the tarmac, a few yards from the bumper.

'Look, Dad,' exclaimed the brothers, 'the beer bottle is following us.'

'I'll do the looking,' said Signora Octavia to her husband. 'You keep your eyes on the road.'

She looked back and saw that the empty orangeade bottle and the empty mineral water bottle had joined the beer bottle to form a bouncing, dancing trio.

'Just like three little dogs,' observed Signorina Rosella, her fiancé nodding in agreement.

'Faster, Dad, faster,' exhorted Angelo and Piero. 'Then we'll be able to shake them off.'

But Signor Zerbini couldn't accelerate because there was another bottle in front of the car. The beer bottle ran behind, clacking over the road's surface, accompanied by a tin of mince and a tin of sliced peaches in syrup – both empty, of course. At that moment, an eight-cylindered American cadillac, with a defiant snort, began to overtake the Zerbinis' modest but practical family car. All the empty bottles joined in the race, leaping, romping, rolling, bouncing and spinning like hoops. Among them was a bottle of Ciro, the local wine, three soda bottles, two sardine tins, a jar of caviar and a dozen paper plates. They sounded like a muffled percussion band.

'Well,' said Signor Zerbini. 'It looks as if it's happening to everything. Imagine what it would have been like if there had been a heavy tyre on the road.'

A long procession of cars was now moving along Via Aurelia, each with its own tail of empties – glass bottles, plastic bottles and milk bottles. Each empty had its own particular clicking sound and its own personal rhythm. They jumped along with tiny steps or great leaps, skidding violently on the hairpin bends. The spectacle was enough to put joy into your heart. Signor Zerbini remembered his boyhood when he had played the plates in the Crash Clatter Band. His uncle had played the bucket and the stove pipe in the same band.

Angelo and Piero were urging their father to slow down so that they could see the vintage cars, sports cars and saloons being pursued by a tail of straw-covered flasks, five- and ten-litre cans and every imaginable kind of receptacle.

Problems arose when they finally got home. The three empties rushed straight into the lift without letting Signora Octavia get in first. They wouldn't keep still for one moment, stamped on the boys' feet, pulled at Rosella's tights and angered young Pierluigi by rummaging in his trouser turn-ups.

It was quite clear by now that the empties would not be satisfied with their excursion. They went into the flat, ran about the corridors and jumped on the beds. The beer bottle lay down under Signor Zerbini's pillow. The orange bottle crawled under Signora Octavia's bedside mat and the bottle of mineral water stretched itself out in the handbasin. There's simply no accounting for tastes!

The children enjoyed themselves; the adults rather less. Rosella was partly consoled by a goodnight telephone call from her fiancé. She told him: 'Do you know, there is an empty tin of tomatoes in my bed? Just think, I always used to eat spaghetti with butter and never liked tomato sauce.'

Boxes, tins and bottles all went to sleep very quickly. They slept without kicking each other or snoring and were no trouble at all. In the morning, they took a bath before anyone else had risen and put the house in apple-pie order. The family – grown-ups and children – went into town: some to school, some to the shops and Signora Octavia to the market. The empties stayed at home. There were four of them now, because a tin of freshly ground coffee had leapt out of the rubbish bin, its label still on, and was doing the washing up in the bath. It made a great deal of noise but didn't break anything.

'It would be just as well if I didn't buy any more tinned food,' Signora Octavia thought to herself. At intervals along the road she met empties going about their errands, making

sure they crossed the road only when the traffic lights were green. She saw a man trying to squash a cardboard shoe box into a litter bin. But no sooner had he turned away than out jumped the box and, tap, tap, tap, followed close behind.

At lunchtime in the Zerbini household the three bottles and the coffee tin were out on the balcony taking the air.

'What do you think they want?' asked Signora Zerbini.

'I think they're trying to fatten themselves up,' replied Signor Zerbini.

'What *do* you mean?'

'Go and see for yourself. The beer bottle has already grown into a two-litre decanter.'

'How big was the coffee tin originally?'

'About half a kilo.'

'Well, it's at least five kilos now.'

'But what can they be eating?' asked Angelo and Piero, who nurtured scientific interests.

'They're empties, so I imagine they feed themselves on emptiness.'

The evening papers confirmed Signor Zerbini's theory. They carried a declaration by a Professor Boxford, the world expert in containers and packaging. He was a lecturer in Boxology at the Polytechnic and in his article he wrote:

'This is a perfectly normal phenomenon. Because of Theory X which as yet we know nothing about, empties the world over are manifesting a tendency to become even emptier. In order to become emptier, they have to become bigger. Is that clear? It will be most interesting to observe whether or not they explode.'

'Woe is me!' exclaimed Signora Octavia, studying the mineral water bottle which had come to sit down beside her on the sofa and was reading the newspaper over her shoulder. 'If they shatter, it will bring us seven years' bad luck.'

After supper, the beer bottle had grown as tall as the refrigerator. The coffee tin was now as large as a cupboard and had half-filled the children's room where, being inquisitive, it had gone to find out what was going on.

'The professor says here that this is a perfectly normal phenomenon,' explained Signor Zerbini. 'It's not a phenomenal phenomenon, although I don't suppose you've heard of phenomenology anyway.'

'No, I can't say I have,' retorted Signora Octavia. 'And since you know so much about it, perhaps you can tell me where we are going to sleep tonight?'

As she spoke, Signora Octavia led her husband to look at their bed which had been taken over by the orange bottle and the beer bottle, sleeping peacefully side by side like two hills swelling the covers. Two corkless necks rested gently on the pillows.

'Well, it's not as bad as all that,' said the head of the family. 'Where there's room for two there's room for four. We can't be too selfish.'

Within a week, the coffee tin had become so big that it occupied the whole of the children's room. The only thing left for them to do was to put their beds and bedside tables inside the tin. Angelo and Piero loved this and played sardines. In Rosella's room, her tube of spot-remover cream had grown so big that it now contained her divan bed, her dressing table, her collection of Great Masters of Art, three vases of dried flowers, her Beatles records, record player, oriental slippers from Sarajevo from her fiancé, the chest she had kept her dolls in as a child and, when he was around, the cat. In the kitchen, the mineral water bottle had had the commonsense to grow lengthways out the window from which it now protruded like the muzzle of a cannon. Other windows in the neighbourhood spouted similar glass cannons but no one seemed to find it at all odd.

In the Zerbinis' bed, the occupying bottles had grown horizontally without disturbing anyone in the slightest. It had its disadvantages of course and the Zerbinis had to climb inside the bottles in order to go to bed. Signora Octavia chose the orange bottle because she couldn't stand the smell of beer. It was a splendid sight seeing them sleeping tranquilly in their bottles, like sailing ships fashioned by old sea salts or carved with infinite patience by prisoners serving life-sentences. At least it would have been a splendid sight but the lights were out and you couldn't see a thing.

The same thing was happening in every house throughout the city. People quickly adapted to going in and out of bottles, jars of marmalade, ice-cream cartons and boxes of sweets. Lawyers received their clients in shoe boxes or biscuit tins. Every family had its own empties, and living in tins didn't seem to present any problems at all.

Rosella and her fiancé now met in a tin of mushrooms in brine, where there was a green bench. (Most places were good for romance and the mushrooms didn't smell too bad.)

Boxes that couldn't find any room in flats camped out in the streets, in the squares and on the hills around the city. The Garibaldi monument was now in a tin of filleted mackerels with the cover rolled back around the tin opener. It held up the traffic a bit but the ever obliging City Council had built a delightful little wooden bridge above it so that cars could cross over with ease.

The television now broadcast live tinnings of the Matterhorn, the Eiffel Tower and Windsor Castle, with a running commentary by the polished television announcer, Tito Stagano.

Meanwhile, back at the Observatory in Bochum, Germany, an astronomer and his colleague from Mount Palomar, USA were exchanging coded information about a singular object far away in space which seemed to be moving towards planet Earth.

'Is it a comet, Professor Box?'

'I wouldn't like to say, Professor Schachtelmacher. I don't have the right equipment.'

'Ah yes, I can see it now,' said Professor Schachtelmacher. 'It has a strange form, rather like a . . .'

'Like what, Professor Schachtelmacher?'

'Well, a box, Professor Box – a large box.'

'You're right – it's a superbox! Large enough to box in both the Earth and the moon, by the look of things . . .'

Three hours later, the whole of the western hemisphere was contained in a tin of anchovies in oil, and smelt faintly of fish.

FOCUS QUESTIONS

1 When Signor Zerbini tells his family not to leave any pieces of paper or rubbish around, what does he really want them to do?

2 What is Angelo and Piero's attitude towards the rubbish they leave behind?

3 How does the family react to the sight of their rubbish following them?

4 Based on the information given in the story, write a definition of a 'Crash Clatter Band'.

5 Explain why 'The children enjoyed themselves; the adults rather less'.

6 Why does Professor Boxford think the empties might explode?

7 What adjustments do people have to make when the empties grow in size?

8 What does the ending suggest is happening in the story?

EXPLORING WORDS

9 Explain the meaning of the underlined words or phrases in the following extracts from the story.

   a 'They made a charming <u>tableau</u> at the foot of the chestnut tree.'

   b 'Faster, Dad, faster, <u>exhorted</u> Angelo.'

   c '. . . an eight-cylindered American cadillac . . . began to overtake the Zerbinis' <u>modest</u> but practical family car.'

   d '. . . every imaginable kind of <u>receptacle</u>.'

   e '. . . put the house in <u>apple-pie</u> order.'

   f '. . . three bottles and the coffee tin were out on the balcony <u>taking the air</u>.'

   g 'It was a splendid sight seeing them sleeping <u>tranquilly</u> in their bottles.'

WRITING

10 Continue writing the story. Will the containers take over completely? Can the people fight back in some way?

11 Write about some other inanimate things coming to life. Some possibilities include:

▶ Flora which has been destroyed (for example, trees that have been chopped down).

▶ Electrical household appliances.

FURTHER ACTIVITIES

12 Imagine you are placed in charge of recycling in your school. What would you do to encourage students to recycle? How would you encourage the school community to participate?

The Chewing-Gum Rescue

On the evening of pocket-money day Mr Frisbee came stumping along to his own back door after shutting up his prize-winning angora goats, Gregorius and Gertrude, for the night. He had been very careful about this for the infamous Gargle Goat Thief Gang was roaming around the countryside, stealing goats of all kinds – very worrying for goat owners. Mr Frisbee was looking forward to a quiet evening with his wife and children. But as he was wiping his weary feet in their faithful gumboots, suddenly the gumboots stuck to the doormat and he fell head-over-heels into the hall.

'Help! Help!' shouted Mr Frisbee as he lay there, his feet up in the air and the doormat still stuck to his boots. His five daughters, Florence, Flora, Fenella, Felicity and the baby Francesca came running to see what had happened to their loving father.

'Oh Dad!' cried Florence. 'You have trodden on a piece of Francesca's chewing-gum.'

'Yes,' said Flora. 'You know, Dad! It's on the telly.'

'It's on the doormat too,' grumbled Mr Frisbee shaking his feet out of their faithful gumboots.

'It's advertised on television,' Flora explained. 'It's Dr Gumption's simply Great Green Gum with the Daily Fresh Mint Flavour.'

'It's full of fluoride and chlorophyll and it's the gum that's good for the gums,' said Felicity.

'And it's got champion chewability,' finished Fenella as she helped Felicity pull the doormat away from the gumboots. It took a lot of doing.

'Can't you have ice-cream instead?' asked Mr Frisbee fretfully.

And Florence, Flora, Felicity, Fenella and even Francesca replied as one daughter, 'Mum won't let us.'

'Of course I won't', said Mrs Frisbee firmly, for she was a dentist during the day, and disapproved of sweets and cakes which, as everyone knows, are so bad for children's teeth. 'No ice-creams in this house, no chocolate or sherbert or coconut cream caramels or butterscotch! No fudge or toffee apples, no brown sugar peanut brittle, and no buttery molasses taffy. Dr Gumption's Gum is the only thing I'm prepared to tolerate. I want all my daughters to have teeth as strong as tigers' teeth and as beautiful as pearls.'

Well, that very night, after the girls had eaten all their greens, chewed their crusts twenty-five times each and had each finished off with a raw carrot, they sat down to watch television. But no sooner had the television set been switched on than Dr Gumption himself appeared, smiling and scraping all over the screen.

'Hey kids!' he cried. 'It's good GOOD news. Dr Gumption has a great new gum on the market and – WOW – it's twice as sticky and – mmmmmmmmmm – it's twice as stretchy and – YAY – it's twice as green and it's got double that super duper minty flavour, so listen kids, to what everyone is saying . . .'

And then a chorus of beautiful girls in green clustered around Dr Gumption and they sang . . .

'Do friends avoid you? Take the hint!
Chew Dr Gumption's Minty-mint.'

'Shall we?' Florence signalled to her sisters by wiggling her crooked eyebrows.

'Next pocket-money day!' Flora signalled back with hers.

Next pocket-money day Mr Frisbee came home after locking up his prize angora goats with tremendous care and he found that the back door wouldn't even open; he had to go round to the front door like a polite visitor. As he came in the smell of minty-mint rolled towards him like a great green ocean.

'What's happened to the back door?' he demanded crossly.

'It's got a piece of Felicity's gum stuck in it,' said Flora, telling tales as she often did.

'Fenella made me put it there,' grumbled Felicity. 'She said . . . "Just for fun put your gum here!" and when I did, she shut the door on it and now we can't get the door open, and my gum has gone for good.'

'Honestly, my dear,' Mr Frisbee said to his wife, 'a simple orange each would save a lot of trouble in the long run.'

'Never!' declared Mrs Frisbee (Dentist). 'I spend all day patching up teeth ruined by coconut candy and frosted cakes. Never shall my daughters feast on brandy balls or barley sugar, Turkish delight, marshmallows or chocolate peanuts.

They shall have teeth as strong as tigers' teeth and as beautiful as pearls.'

But later, when the lid of the piano refused to open because Francesca's gum was jammed under it, Mrs Frisbee looked very thoughtful and still later, when the tablecloth stuck to the table just as if it had been nailed at all four corners, she looked quite cross.

That very night on television the beaming face of Dr Gumption appeared once more.

'Hey kids, hey!' he shouted. 'Boy oh boy! What news! Dr Gumption's Gum has been improved yet again. Triple Chewability! Quadruple stretch power. Ten times the stick-ability! Oh that gloptious Gumption Gum. It's the NOW gum! It's the POW gum! And don't forget, kids, it's got that triple ripple super duper minty-mint flavour.' And the girls in green appeared and sang . . .

> 'Make your father go all numb!
> Chew Dr Gumption's Gloptious Gum!'

'Shall we?' signalled Florence with her crooked eyebrows.

'Yes, yes, yes!' signalled Flora, Felicity, Fenella, and Francesca.

A week later on pocket-money day Mr Frisbee came home having shut his precious Gregorius and Gertrude away for the night.

'The Gargle Gang will never get them,' he muttered fiercely to himself. 'But locking up is hard work. I'm longing for a cup of tea.' He stumped up the path in his faithful gumboots but he could not open the back door or the front door either. Most of the windows were sealed shut, too, but at last he found that he could open the bathroom window with a stick, and by standing on an up-ended apple box he was able to somersault into his house.

Inside, the smell of Super Duper Minty-mint was so strong he staggered back clutching his throat. Dr Gumption's chewing-gum stretched everywhere in an evil green web. It was as if a whole houseful of wicked spiders had been at work for a week. It seized your shoes and stuck them to the floor, it caught your coat and held on to your hair. It was like a super duper minty-mint mad monster from Mars stretching from room to room to room to room.

'Arrrrrh!' cried Mr Frisbee, as his five daughters and Mrs Frisbee came to meet him, climbing nimbly through the sticky maze. 'Couldn't you let them have a liquorice all-sort each instead?' he gasped.

'No, no!' replied Mrs Frisbee. 'I'm a dentist as well as a mother. If you saw the horrors that I see every day – molars molested and melted away by refined sugars – you would understand. Never shall my little ones have peppermint creams or coconut ice, boiled lollies, dolly mixtures, raspberry drops, wine gums, humbugs, jujubes or all-day suckers. My daughters must have teeth as strong as tigers' teeth and as beautiful as pearls.'

'I suppose they must,' said Mr Frisbee wearily.

At dinner that night the soup tasted of Dr Gumption's Super Duper Minty-mint Gum. The roast beef, roast potatoes, roast onions, roast parsnips, roast pumpkin and buttered beans all tasted of Dr Gumption's Super Duper Minty-mint Gum and so did the wholesome apple brown-betty and the raw carrots to finish off with. No one enjoyed anything very much.

Yet that very night on television Dr Gumption appeared again. 'Hey kids!' he shouted. 'Hey – all you gum chewers out there! Have you tried Dr Gumption's NEW splendiferous magniferous gum? Such expansion. Such extension! It stretches up and out and every whichever way. It's the fun gum that keeps the household happy and healthy. It sticks so well that it's being used by boat builders as a saltwater glue. And it's got that unutterable, that entirely inexpressible super duper triple ripple more-minty-than-mint flavour. WOW!'

Then the girls in green appeared and sang . . .

> 'Want to make your teacher squint?
> Chew Dr Gumption's Minty-mint.'

'Next time!' Florence signalled Flora, Felicity, Fenella and Francesca, wiggling her eyebrows in time to the music.

A week later on pocket-money day Mr Frisbee staggered up to bed coughing and choking and fighting off green tentacles of gum.

'Man can triumph over any odds,' he muttered. 'He can get used to anything if he has to.' He was a bit lonely because Mrs Frisbee was out at a Dental Health Conference.

What Mr Frisbee did not know was that Florence, Flora, Felicity, Fenella and even Francesca all had packets of Dr Gumption's New More-minty-than-mint Gum tucked under their pillows. They hadn't started chewing it yet because they had some of the old Triple Minty-mint Gum from last week's pocket-money day to use up first.

As he lay awake, missing Mrs Frisbee B.D.S., Mr Frisbee heard strange shufflings and muffled bleats coming from the goat pens. They were not very loud and, had Mrs Frisbee been at home, he would have been sound asleep and would have missed hearing them altogether. As it was he leaped to his feet and peeped out of the window. What a sight met his eyes!

There were the five dreadful Gargle brothers, leaders of the Gargle Goat Thief Gang, not to mention five of their minions. They were in the actual act of stealing Gregorious and Gertrude, Mr Frisbee's prize-winning angoras. There was not a moment to be lost.

Wrapping his hands in Mrs Frisbee's second-best petticoat and seizing a strand of Doctor Gumption's Triple Super Duper Minty-mint Gum that happened to be dangling from the guttering, Mr Frisbee swung down like Tarzan, a curiously splendid figure in his simulated leopardskin pyjamas, screaming reprimands and reproaches at the villainous goat thieves.

Florence and Flora woke up at once and looked out of the window. What they saw horrified them and they hastened to wake up Felicity, Fenella and even Francesca by way of reinforcements. Armed only with Dr Gumption's New More-minty-than-mint Gum, they climbed out of the bathroom window and whisked over to the goat pens.

For there was no doubt that Mr Frisbee was getting the worst of it.

In his first spectacular swing he had struck Harvey Gargle to the ground and then as he swept majestically back he had struck Ellis Gargle, knocking out his false teeth and seriously bewildering him. But then he himself hit the side of the house very hard and let go the chewing-gum, falling dazed to the ground, an easy prey to the infuriated goat thieves.

Mad Rory Gargle with two minions advanced upon him in a threatening way; Bernard Gargle (with two other minions) picked up his fallen brothers, not forgetting Ellis's false teeth, while Rackham Gargle with the single remaining minion rapidly led Gregorious Goat and his nanny wife, Gertrude, towards a waiting van.

Victory was within the grasp of the nefarious goat thieves. All seemed lost . . .

When, suddenly, with a lion-like roar Florence sprang out at them from the right, biting firmly into a piece of Dr Gumption's New More-minty-than-mint gum as she did so. Flora bounded in from the left, whooping and hooting like a whole treeful of owls. There was a hearty hullabaloo from Fenella who, chewing her piece of Dr Gumption's Mintier-than-mint Gum, came up behind Florence, a blood-curdling growl from Felicity leaping out of the chrysanthemums, and squeaks and squeals from Francesca who rose up out of the watering-can.

The goat thieves were entirely taken aback. This unexpected racket and rumpus-bumpus upset them badly.

'Squad . . . breathe OUT!' shouted Florence and the daughters of the house breathed out as one combined daughter. A terrible wave of unutterable, indescribable, inexpressible, super duper triple ripple more-minty-than-mint aroma swept over the goat thieves.

'Enemy Mint Gas Attack!' shouted Mad Rory Gargle before he dropped like a stone. Lewis and Rackham Gargle and the

assorted minions keeled over like slender reeds in a hurricane and even the goats fell to their knees gasping.

Mr Frisbee, however, had been exposed to Dr Gumption's punishing mint flavour for at least three weeks and although somewhat unsteady, he was not totally overcome. He had built up an immunity.

'Tie them up!' he ordered. 'Quickly.'

His devoted daughters did not hesitate. Within a moment the Gargle Gang were wound around with Dr Gumption's powerful product. The music died down and the goats began to revive. At this very moment Mrs Frisbee drove the family car into the yard. She was astonished to find it filled with disabled goat thieves, groggy goats, her husband bruised but resplendent in his simulated leopardskin pyjamas, not to mention her five daughters still up well beyond their bedtime.

'You see how wise I was,' she said. 'You couldn't have saved Gregorius and Gertrude with a piece of Turkish delight.'

'I'll never say anything against Dr Gumption's Mintier-than-mint Gum again,' Mr Frisbee vowed fervently.

Florence looked at her sisters. 'Shall I tell him?' she signalled with her crooked eyebrows.

'O.K.,' they all signalled back.

'Actually Dad,' said Florence, 'we're getting rather sick of it.'

'Well, that's all right, my dear,' said Mrs Frisbee quickly, 'because I heard of a delicious new sweet at the Conference today. Honey Bliss it's called and it's made with pure golden honey collected from lime blossoms by particularly happy and busy bees. Of course you'll still have to brush your teeth after it, but you have to do that anyway.'

Florence, Flora, Felicity, Fenella and Francesca looked delighted to hear this. They had enjoyed Dr Gumption's Gum but it was very hard work keeping it under control and they needed a rest.

The police came and took the goat thieves away. 'We've been waiting a long time to get our hands on this lot,' the Chief Constable said. 'There's a big reward, you know. You'll be able to extend your herd of angora goats.'

Mr Frisbee, though bruised and battered, beamed with joy.

Shortly after this Dr Gumption's Gum was withdrawn from the market and only used again in army exercises. Florence, Flora, Felicity, Fenella and Francesca settled down with Honey Bliss which smelt deliciously of lime blossom and tasted wonderful. However, it must be noted that when Gertrude the goat had two beautiful kids a short time later they did have, very faintly, a mintier-than-mint perfume, no doubt due to their mother's exposure to Dr Gumption's Gum during the great mintier-than-mint goat rescue and the heroic victory of the Frisbee sisters, all of whom grew up to have teeth as strong as tigers' teeth and as beautiful as pearls.

FOCUS QUESTIONS

1 Why is Mr Frisbee keen to make sure that his goats are safely locked up at night?

2 For what reasons does Mrs Frisbee allow her children to eat Dr Gumption's chewing-gum but forbid them to eat sweets and cakes?

3 What other evidence can you find to suggest that this family is very concerned about both health and cleanliness?

4 In what respects are Dr Gumption's new gums improvements on the earlier variety?

5 Despite Mrs Frisbee's approval of the chewing-gum, is there anything to suggest that she had some doubts about its use?

6 What is your view of Mr Frisbee as both father and husband. Support your opinion with close reference to the text. For example, what is the significance of his statement: 'Man can triumph over any odds . . . He can get used to anything if he has to.'

EXPLORING WORDS

7 Match the following words from the story with their meanings in the second column.

Words from the story

a '. . . not to mention five of their <u>minions</u>.'
b '. . . screaming <u>reprimands</u> and reproaches.'
c '. . . the <u>villainous</u> goat thieves.'
d '. . . they <u>hastened</u> to wake up Felicity.'
e '. . . knocking out his false teeth and seriously <u>bewildering</u> him.'
f '. . . the <u>nefarious</u> goat thieves.'
g 'He had built up an <u>immunity</u>.'
h 'She was <u>astonished</u> to find it filled.'
i '. . . her husband bruised but <u>resplendent</u>.'

Meanings

Greatly surprised.
Perplexing, puzzling.
Hurried.
Wicked.
Very wicked.
A servant or follower.
Protection from disease.
Criticise or rebuke.
Brilliant, splendid.

WRITING

8   Write the next 'chapter' of this story – explaining the ways in which Honey Bliss proves to be of great benefit to the whole family.

9   Prepare the advertising campaign for Honey Bliss. To do this you will need to:

   ▶ Make a list of the main **characteristics** of the product – you must be clear about what will attract people to it.

   ▶ Consider the **price** you will charge for the product.

   ▶ Discuss the **audience** for the advertisements. Who will the product appeal to?

   ▶ Decide what **form** the campaign will take – newspapers, posters, radio, television – as this will affect the material you prepare.

They'll Never Find You Now

H idden behind the thick hedge, Sweeney studied the cottage and the old woman pottering in its garden.

The dilapidated cottage seemed to be fighting a losing battle with the encroaching vegetation. Small wonder if the bent old woman who was snipping at flowers and shrubs was the only gardener.

Sweeney had come across the place only by accident, having taken a wrong turning and landed himself in a maze of winding and ever-narrowing lanes. When the stolen mini had suddenly acquired a puncture he had pushed it off the road into a thicket, taken his suitcase and, cursing his bad luck, gone forward on foot.

The lane had been knobbly as a knuckleduster under his thin city shoes, and he had seen no habitation of any kind until he had come upon the cottage.

The old woman hobbled back indoors with her basket of cuttings, and the only remaining sign of life was a large black cat sunning itself on the doorstep.

Sweeney shuffled his aching feet and weighed the pros and cons. All his instincts told him the woman lived alone – he could scent loneliness and defencelessness as quickly as he could smell a peeled orange – and he had to hide somewhere for a while.

Cautiously Sweeney followed the hedge round to the back. There was another neglected strip of garden with a nanny goat tethered to a post and a few hens scratching about in a wire run. Self-sufficient this old girl – and Sweeney reckoned she needed to be, living as she did in such isolation. He made up his mind; the cottage might be a bit short on the mod cons but it offered safety.

His double-cross would have been discovered by now and the gang would be searching for him. They would never find him here, that was certain. He would wait long enough for them to think he had slipped through the net and got out of the country, then he would make his way down to the coast where the fisherman who had ferried Vickie across the channel was waiting to make a second trip with him.

Sweeney sweated a little as he thought of Vickie – blonde, beautiful, and waiting for him to join her with the proceeds of the robbery. Not just his share but the whole of the cash. She was worth the risk he had taken but he valued his neck too much to spoil everything for want of a bit of patience now.

He picked up his case and went round to the front again. The cat, seeing him come up the path, stretched itself lazily and slipped ahead of him into the cottage.

Sweeney stood in the doorway, his big frame blocking out the light, and stared assessingly around. The room was cluttered but comparatively clean and had a pleasant, garden-like perfume from bunches of mint, thyme, and other herbs which hung drying from the mantelshelf.

The old woman had frozen into an animal stillness, her hands motionless amongst the blossoms spread on the table. She was even older than he had thought, just skin and bones. Only her bright, monkey-brown eyes showed any vitality.

'Good afternoon,' Sweeney said, playing it cool. 'May I use your phone?'

'There is no phone here.' The voice was a rusty croak.

'Well, maybe your husband or son could give me a hand to get the car back on the road?'

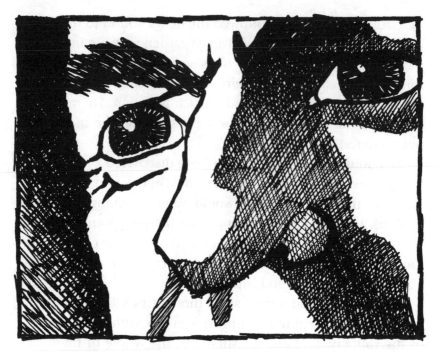

She shook her head. 'There is nobody but me here.'

Sweeney reached behind him and closed the cottage door.

The woman's hand fluttered to her throat. 'What do you want?'

'Just board and lodging for a while.' Sweeney nodded towards an ancient sofa. 'That will do if you haven't got a spare bed.'

The old eyes studied Sweeney's face, registering its brutality and the bleak coldness of his prominent, heavy-lidded eyes.

'Nobody would want to stay here ... unless they were trying to hide.'

'That's about it, Grandma.' He was moving about the room, opening drawers and cupboards. They contained nothing but an eccentric old country woman's collection of junk. There was nothing to make him doubt that she lived alone.

'Are the police looking for you?'

Sweeney grinned. 'Yeah, them too – but it's more my friends I'm concerned about at the moment. If they get their hands on me after what I've done ...' His grin vanished and he gripped the old woman's shoulder, making her wince. 'Do you have any visitors here? The truth now – or I'll make you regret it.'

She surprised him with a cackle of laughter. 'Visitors? Who'd want to visit me? There is not a soul within miles.'

'That's what I thought. How come you live here all on your own like this?'

'I was born here.' All at once she seemed to accept Sweeney's presence as inevitable. 'There were other cottages scattered around here then. But times change. There is only me left now. Me and Blackie.'

The cat, which had been sitting quietly at her feet, looked up and acknowledged its name with a soft mew.

Sweeney sat down in one of the two fireside chairs, the suitcase full of money placed carefully within reach.

Just so that the old girl should know the score right from the start he took his revolver out of his pocket and examined it nonchalantly. Fear flickered in the woman's eyes and Sweeney put the gun away again casually, as if it had been a cigarette lighter.

'I want food and a place to sleep. You won't come to any harm so long as you do as you are told – but don't cross me, see?'

She nodded and returned to her sorting of flowers and leaves. Her gnarled hands were trembling but she obviously wasn't the hysterical type. That suited Sweeney. He didn't want to have to knock her about – she was too frail to stand up to it and he couldn't afford to have that complication along with everything else.

Time, Sweeney decided a couple of hours later, was going to be his biggest problem here. It was going to drag so much it would drive him up the wall with boredom. The old woman didn't even have a radio let alone television.

Sweeney pushed his plate away and sat picking his teeth disconsolately. His meal had been surprisingly good – an omelette made with eggs fresh from the hens and fragrant with herbs, accompanied by homemade bread and cheese. He had realised that his unwilling hostess must be some sort of back-to-nature crank – but he didn't mind going back to nature if it resulted in food that tasted like that.

But how was he going to kill time? He saw himself cooped up in the cottage, perhaps for weeks, with not even a drink to relieve the monotony – and suddenly the hideout didn't seem such a good idea after all.

He went out to the little scullery where the old woman, who had said she would have her own meal later, tended a pot bubbling on the stove.

It was a mystery to Sweeney how she could cook so well on anything so ancient. Flames leaped and spluttered from its rusty iron top, filling the place with a scarlet glow.

'Hell!' Sweeney's voice was truculent. 'I don't suppose you have even got a drink in this God-forsaken hole!'

The old woman looked at him in silence for a moment, then shuffled across to open a cupboard door.

Sweeney, glimpsing bottles of homemade wines, pushed her aside and began rummaging. Beetroot, dandelion, elderberry and, more to his fancy, a bottle labelled 'sloe gin.'

'Get me a glass,' Sweeney ordered, and took the bottle back with him to the big fireside chair.

'That's strong stuff, Grandma!' Sweeney nodded his approval. The gin was as smooth as silk but with a kick like dynamite.

For the first time since his arrival the old woman smiled.

'In the old days,' she boasted, 'people used to come from miles around for my sloe gin – and other things I used to make for them.'

'I can believe it.' Sweeney refilled his glass. Once again he found himself thinking how monkey-like the old woman's eyes were – bright, and with a kind of sly mischievousness lurking in their brown depths.

He could have snapped her in two with his bare hands, he told himself, but it was always as well to be cautious. He placed his gun to hand on the table.

'Drunk or sober, I can put a bullet in you,' he said. 'So don't get any ideas.'

'An old woman like me?' She looked at him for a moment, then went out to the scullery again.

Sweeney smiled and refilled his glass. The cottage was quite cosy at night with the firelight flickering on the copper kettle and brass fire irons.

'I've done all right for myself,' Sweeney said, addressing the cat curled up in the chair opposite.

'What's that you are cooking, Ma?' Sweeney could see the old woman bent over the pot oblivious to the steam wreathing about her face.

'Oh, just a pinch of this and a scrap of that.' The rusty old voice seemed to come from far away.

'Smells good,' Sweeney said and he was amused to hear himself having trouble pronouncing the words. His glass was empty so he filled it again and drank in silence for a while. He had begun to feel quite lethargic although drink didn't usually affect him that way.

He watched the cat uncurl itself and arch its back in a long, luxurious stretch. It began purring and, with its emerald eyes fixed on Sweeney, it clawed at the chair cushion, moving its paws one after the other in a soft, padding, feline kind of dance.

Sweeney shook his head, trying to clear it. The old woman was singing in the scullery, her voice cracked and shrill.

'Shut up,' Sweeney said. But the old woman took no notice, just went on stirring the pot and chanting – it wasn't really singing – and despite his bemused senses Sweeney was chillingly aware that he didn't like the words.

The cat's purring grew louder, a rumbling accompaniment to its mistress's chant.

Sweeney tried to rise from his chair but found that he couldn't. He felt so . . . peculiar. A kind of strange disturbance was taking place within him – a kaleidoscopic rearrangement of molecule and cell.

The old woman came in from the scullery, the cat stopped its purring, and together they looked at the small green frog with the protuberant eyes so like Sweeney's that squatted now in Sweeney's chair.

'Come along, little 'un,' the old woman said. She carried the frog to the front door and placed it on the step. It stayed still, its bulging eyes gazing mournfully upwards, until she put her foot under its rear and flipped it on to the path – then it went hopping off into the undergrowth.

'That's it, my dear, off you go,' said the old woman. 'And if it's any consolation – they'll never find you now.'

FOCUS QUESTIONS

1   a   Summarise (in point form) the reasons why Sweeney decides to stay at the old woman's cottage.

    b   Make a separate list of the disadvantages and problems Sweeney considers.

2   Write a description of the old woman and her lifestyle. Include details of:
    ▶ Where she lives.
    ▶ Her physical appearance.
    ▶ Her cat.
    ▶ Her laugh.
    ▶ The things she makes and the equipment she uses.

3   The tension in this story builds up as we come to suspect that the woman is a witch. To achieve this, the story draws on some of our knowledge of fairy tales (for example, 'Hansel and Gretel'). What do such stories have in common with this story?

EXPLORING WORDS

4   Explain the meaning of the following extracts from the story, paying particular attention to the underlined words.

    a   'The dilapidated cottage seemed to be fighting a losing battle with the encroaching vegetation.'

    b   'Self-sufficient this old girl – and Sweeney reckoned she needed to be.'

    c   'All at once she seemed to accept Sweeney's presence as inevitable.'

    d   'He didn't want to have to knock her about – she was too frail . . . and he couldn't afford to have that complication along with everything else.'

    e   'A kind of strange disturbance was taking place within him – a kaleidoscopic rearrangement of molecule and cell.'

WRITING

5   Imagine that the next person who arrives at the cottage knows all about the old woman, and has magic powers of his or her own. Write about what happens.

6   Write a sequel to the story, describing what happens when either Vickie or the police arrive at the old woman's cottage.

FURTHER ACTIVITIES

7   Produce a 'Wanted' poster for Sweeney, including as much information as you can about his crime, accomplices, appearance, suspected whereabouts, and so on. (Note: Your information must be drawn from the story.)

The Boy Who Wouldn't Get Out of the Pool

There was once a boy who loved swimming.

He loved to jump in, making the water splash high above him. He loved to duck-dive and to glide along the bottom, touching the black lines. Most of all, he loved to stay in when all the rest of his family had got out and was dressed ready to go home.

'Come on,' they said. 'You'll make us late. You can't stay in all day.'

'But I want to ,' he said as he climbed out at the silver steps.

One day the sun seemed hotter than usual. The water was cool and blue. The boy jumped higher, dived deeper and swam further than ever before. One by one, the members of his family got out, dressed and sat waiting for him.

'Come on,' they said. 'You'll make us late.'

But the boy kept diving and swimming.

'You'll get cold,' called his mother.

The boy laughed.

'Your skin will go wrinkly,' yelled his sister.

He laughed again.

His grandmother sat back on the wooden seat and folded her hands in her lap.

'You'll turn into a fish,' she said, coldly.

He dived away from them.

'We're leaving,' they called. 'We really mean it.'

And they did.

When the boy came up from the bottom of the pool, they were gone.

At first the boy didn't care. He glided along the bottom of the pool and touched three black lines before he came up to breathe. He climbed out and jumped back in again seven times, each time making a bigger splash than the time before. And he swam across, only stopping twice.

At the end of all this, he sat on the edge of the pool and looked down at his hands. The skin wasn't wrinkly. It was clean and shiny. But he was feeling cold, so he wrapped himself in his towel and followed his family home.

After dinner he went to his room. He still felt as cold as if he had just stepped out of the water. He ran his smooth hands through his hair and looked in the mirror. He eyes were shiny and more widely spaced than before. He turned away but one eye kept looking at him as he stood in the middle of the carpet and dived into his bed.

His mother nodded to him when he came down to breakfast the next morning, but said nothing. She didn't notice the bumps that he could feel pressing under his T-shirt. His mouth pushed forward like an O as he ate and he found he could sit facing his sister while still looking at his grandmother in her chair by the window. She was watching him.

He felt more and more uncomfortable and held his spoon awkwardly, spilling some of his food down over his chest.

'Are you going swimming?' she said, as he got up from the table.

'Yes.'

'Don't stay in too long.' Her words seemed to float to him across the quiet room.

He kept feeling uncomfortable until he got to the pool. He leaped in and felt the cool water rush over him. He pushed off from the wall and glided along the bottom. He wriggled his body and turned easily, moving forward over one black line, then two, three, four. He felt no need to come to the surface. He changed direction and headed for the deep end. His body was as cold as the water. He glanced back over his shoulder. He had fins and a tail and he was swimming more smoothly and more quickly than he had ever swum in his life.

He got out and walked quickly to the change room. People kept talking. No one stared. He stood in front of the full length mirror, his skin wet and shiny. An old man brushed past him on his way to the shower. He didn't notice that a sharp fin stood out from the boy's shoulders and back and a tail hung down between his legs. As the boy stared at them they began to fade. He felt them grow lighter until gradually he could no longer see them or feel them. He knew that the minute he dived into the water, they would return.

All summer he stayed at the pool. When the other children raced into the park to play cricket and rounders, he swam. When the sound of the ice-cream van drew everyone from the pool, he dived and thrashed his tail and headed for the bottom. And when it rained and the others stayed home in front of the television set, he swam alone.

Each day he went further, faster. His tail lengthened and the shiny scales that stretched the length of his belly glistened more brightly. Still no one noticed him as he ran from the water to stand in the change room, and stare at himself in the mirror. Each day it seemed to him that it took longer and longer for the fins and tail to fade.

One day his chest hurt. He began coughing as he left the water and only when he felt that he would fall unconscious to the floor, did his breath return.

But he still kept on. His cold body came alive in the water. He darted from one side of the pool to the other. Faster and faster he swam, his body making no sound and causing no waves to ripple along the surface. When he grew tired he glided along the bottom or rolled over and floated easily in the green coolness. He stayed in longer and longer, delaying the time when he had to emerge into the air.

Winter came. The pool closed. The boy stayed in his room and was miserable. He lay on his bed and stared at the wall and grew thinner and thinner. He looked in the mirror and saw that his shiny skin had grown dull. One day his mother said, 'Come on. You can't stay here till next season. Get up. Go out. Find a new sport. Go jogging.'

At first the boy took no notice. Then, one day just to please her, he put on his track suit and jogged slowly around the block. He felt hot and puffed. His legs ached and he

developed a blister on one heel. But the next day he did it again. And the next. As he ran, he breathed deeply, his shoulders relaxed and his legs grew stronger. Soon he was running around the park, to the shops and back and as far as the edge of town.

One evening, he ran for hours around the block. As he passed the house for the third time, his mother called him to come in for his dinner.

'Come on,' she said. 'We'll start eating without you.'

He waved and kept running. The cold wind blew against his face. His cheeks were red. His heart was thumping in his chest as he disappeared around the corner.

'You'll exhaust yourself,' she called as he appeared again.

He laughed and kept running.

'You'll damage your muscles,' said his sister the next time he came round. He laughed again. He tossed his head and for a moment he ran on the spot, his feet clattering on the hard surface of the footpath. His hair blew back over his broad shoulder.

As he galloped on, his grandmother leaned out of an upstairs window. Her voice was high pitched and was carried to him on the wind.

'You'll turn into a horse', she said.

FOCUS QUESTIONS

1   List, in correct order, the changes that take place in the boy's physical appearance.

EXPLORING WORDS

2   The following extract contains factual errors as well as spelling and punctuation mistakes. Rewrite the extract, making any corrections you consider necessary, before you check the original text on pages 79–80.
   a   come on they said youll make us late
   b   but the boy kept diveing and swimming
   c   youll get cold called his sister
   d   the boy larfed
   e   youre skin will go wrinkely yelled his mother
   f   he larfed again
   g   His granmother sat back on the wooden seat and folded her hands in her lap
   h   Youll turn intoa fish she said coldly
   i   he dived a way from them
   j   Were leaveing they called. we rearly it.
   k   And they did.
   l   when the boy came up from the bottom off the pool, they were gone.

WRITING

3   Write the sequel to this story, explaining what happens to the boy as he continues with his running.

4   Write another story modelled on 'The Boy Who Wouldn't Get Out of the Pool', beginning with one of the following lines:
   ❱   There was a boy/girl who loved singing.
   ❱   There was a boy/girl who loved walking slowly.
   ❱   There was a man/woman who was always complaining.
   ❱   There was a man/woman who was always laughing.

5   Write a story with the following title: 'The Family Who Watched TV All the Time'.

Freddie Martin and the Shopping Machine

*N*o one in the Martin family mentioned inventions for about three months, after Freddie's disaster with the dog-washing machine, which had stripped his dog of hair. Even Freddie hadn't mentioned them, and inventing was his favourite hobby. But, on Freddie's birthday, a large parcel from his grandfather arrived in the mail.

Imagine Freddie's joy when he discovered that the box contained just what he'd always wanted . . . an electronics kit.

The first thing he thought of making was a homework machine. He hated doing homework. He'd much rather spend his time inventing things. The homework machine didn't work. At first all it did was screw up paper and break pens and throw things around the room. He didn't need a machine to help him do that. He could do those sorts of things himself, especially when he had homework to do.

He made some adjustments to the machine and got it to work, in a sort of fashion. But it wrote oddly. The O's looked like sausages, the F's looked like pitchforks, the Q's looked like pigs with their curly little tails, and the W's came out upside down. Freddie did put in one piece of the machine's work to his teacher, but the teacher said his writing was terrible. He decided he might be better off doing the homework himself.

He was just pulling the machine to pieces when his mother came home with the shopping. Freddie went to help her because he always liked to see what she had bought. When they had finished carrying in the groceries Freddie's mother slumped into a chair, exhausted.

'I hate shopping,' she said.

Suddenly Freddie knew what he could do with his electronics kit. He could build something that would help his mother, just as she'd helped Stinky when Freddie's dog-washing machine had pulled all his fur off. She'd knitted Stinky a nice colourful coat. He could help his mother by making her a shopping machine.

When Freddie told his mother what he was going to build for her, she said she didn't want a shopping machine. She said she didn't mind shopping all *that* much. What she really meant was that she didn't want Freddie to invent anything for her, because Freddie's inventions always turned out to be disasters.

Freddie decided to build the machine anyway. He would build it in secret, and make it a surprise for her.

Freddie went down to his friend Prof's house. Prof would help him to build the shopping machine, and they could build it in Prof's garage. Then his mother wouldn't know about it and it could be a surprise for her.

Prof said he would help, and came up with quite a few ideas that Freddie hadn't thought of, like a big bell that rang every time a shopkeeper gave the machine the wrong change. Prof was called Prof – which was short for professor – because he wore big glasses and knew a lot about science, and because he was always doing experiments and inventing things. Prof loved inventing things, just like Freddie. That's why they were such good friends.

Prof's mother didn't like him inventing things either and it took quite a while for them to talk her into letting them use the garage. She still remembered the time when Prof had invented the house-painting machine which had ripped all the boards off the outside of the house and then punched big holes through the walls and poured tins of paint into the house over her new carpet.

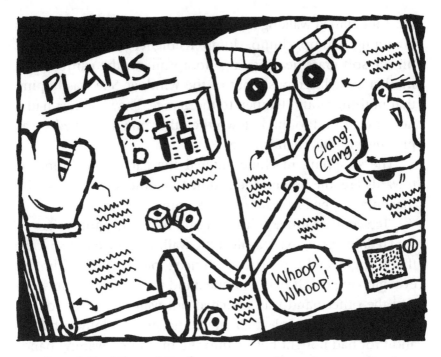

It took Freddie and Prof over two weeks to draw up the plans. They were very complicated and took up a whole exercise book.

When they had finished the plans they started building the machine. They worked very slowly and made sure that everything was right. They didn't want this machine to be a disaster like the other ones they had built.

The hardest part was getting the machine to speak properly. The words sounded funny. When the machine said 'ten cents of lollies, please', it came out sounding like 'this is a holdup, freeze'. Freddie and Prof wanted to send the machine over to the shop for lots of lollies, and they didn't want the shopkeeper to think it was a holdup every time they did.

At last they got the voice to work properly and everything was finished. The shopping machine was ready to go into action. They were both a bit nervous. They didn't want anything to go wrong so they decided to test it first.

They set up a counter in the corner of the garage and Freddie pretended to be a shopkeeper. Prof took the machine out into the yard and told it where to go and what he wanted. The machine started walking towards the garage. Freddie could hear it coming. Clump, clump, clump. Its big feet came down hard on the soft grass, leaving large footprints in the earth. Prof's mother stared nervously out of the window. She was hoping that nothing would happen to the garage. They had just had a new one built. Prof had blown the other one up while he was playing with his chemistry set.

The shopping machine entered the garage and rumbled towards Freddie behind the counter. Freddie felt nervous. The machine stopped in front of the counter.

'Ten cents of lollies, please,' it said in a loud, gruff voice.

Freddie shrank back against the wall. The voice was so loud that it frightened him. The machine stood in front of him, its eyes glowing red. It held out one hand with the ten cents in it, and the other hand was stretched out waiting for the lollies. Freddie came forward, frightened, and put the lollies that he and Prof had bought before into the machine's waiting hand. The other hand dropped the ten cents onto the counter. Then the machine turned around and clomped out and gave the lollies to Prof.

Freddie and Prof sat down on the lawn and ate the lollies as a celebration. Their machine had worked. They were very happy. It was time to try it out for real now.

They decided to try it out at their corner shop. The corner shop was owned by Mr Grumpy. That wasn't his real name. That was just what Freddie and Prof called him, because he was so unfriendly and nasty to them all the time and always gave them the wrong change.

They asked Prof's mother if she wanted anything at the shop. She said she wanted a loaf of bread. They went out and set the machine to go to the shop to get a loaf of bread.

It clomped off down the street towards the shop, holding a two dollar note tightly in its hand. A nasty dog heard it coming and went out to bite whoever was coming down the street. When it saw the machine it stopped and stared, too frightened to move. The dog had chased many people, but it had never seen a person that looked like this before. The machine just kept walking. The dog was frozen to the spot. The machine stepped on its tail and the dog let out a loud yelp and ran into its house. It never ever ran out to bite anyone again.

The machine rumbled across the road and into the shop. Mr Grumpy saw it coming and was frightened. He thought the Martians had landed. But what would a Martian be doing with a big basket on the front of it? He stared with wide eyes as the strange machine came into his shop.

'Wh. . wh. . what do you want?' he asked nervously.

'One loaf of bread, please,' the machine boomed out.

Mr Grumpy quickly got the loaf of bread and put it in the basket on the front of the strange machine. The machine handed over the two dollars and Mr Grumpy gave it the change.

Suddenly, bells started to ring and cymbals clanged and lights flashed. Mr Grumpy was really scared. The thing was going mad. It would wreck his shop.

'Wrong change . . . wrong change . . . wrong change . . . ,' the machine yelled.

Mr Grumpy quickly worked out the right change and gave it to the machine.

'Thank you,' the machine said gruffly, 'see you later.'

The machine turned around and left the shop. Mr Grumpy closed the shop and went to bed. He had bad dreams that night and the next day he sold the shop. He didn't want to serve machines.

Freddie and Prof were delighted. Their machine had worked and it had taught Mr Grumpy a lesson at the same time. They decided to give the machine a real test. It was time to let it go to the supermarket.

They showed Freddie's mother the shopping machine and she was really surprised. She laughed when she heard what had happened at Mr Grumpy's. She didn't like Mr Grumpy either. He always sent home stale bread when she sent Freddie to the shop. She wasn't very keen on letting the machine do her shopping but Freddie and Prof pestered her and at last she said she would write out a shopping list.

The machine took the list and the money and went off towards the shop. Freddie and Prof followed behind, just to make sure that everything went all right.

The machine got to the supermarket without trouble and everything was going smoothly. The first problem came at the turnstile. The machine couldn't fit through. But it soon solved that. It ripped the whole turnstile out and walked through. The people in the shop heard the loud noise and looked to see where it was coming from. Women screamed and children started crying when they saw the huge machine coming towards them.

'We're being invaded by robots,' a woman yelled, 'run for your lives.'

People started running from the store. The manager hurried out to see what all the noise was about, and quickly scuttled back into his office when he saw the huge metal object coming up the aisle towards him. But the machine wasn't upset by all the noise. It went calmly up and down the rows of shelves, picking

out the things that Freddie's mother had put on the list and putting them in its basket. The manager was frantically ringing the fire brigade.

Freddie and Prof couldn't understand what all the noise was about. They thought their machine was beautiful. People shouldn't be scared of it. People would get used to seeing machines doing the shopping if this one worked. They were going to make lots of them and sell them.

When the fire brigade came they peeped cautiously around the corner. The manager had told them that there was a huge monster wrecking his supermarket. The fire chief saw the machine coming down the aisle towards them.

'Turn on the hoses, men,' he shouted. 'We'll soon stop this big bundle of nuts and bolts.'

They turned the hose on and the fire chief himself aimed the water at the machine. As soon as the water hit the machine there was a big flash of blue flame. Freddie and Prof tried to stop the fire chief from hosing their machine, but it was too late. The machine had blown a fuse. Even Prof and Freddie didn't know what would happen now.

The machine went wild. Its eyes flashed, bells rang, cymbals clanged, gears whirred, sprockets sprang, nuts popped, wires twisted and a loud noise was coming from its mouth that sounded like a thousand bullfrogs all croaking at the same time.

It threw frozen chickens and packets of flour. It chucked pizza pies and packets of jelly. It hurled lumps of cheese and ripe tomatoes. It flung pickled onions and packets of peas.

And then there was a loud bang. The machine slumped to the floor.

The supermarket was a mess. Shelves had been thrown to the floor and there were broken packets of food all over the place. One fireman had been hit on the leg with a frozen chicken and was limping badly. The fire chief had been hit with a large bag of flour. It had mixed with the water and he looked like a big lump of dough.

'You killed our machine,' Freddie said.

'Aha, so you're the one who's responsible for this,' the manager said, 'you've wrecked my beautiful supermarket.'

Freddie and Prof got into a lot of trouble. Their parents had to pay a lot of money to have everything fixed up. Freddie had his pocket money cut off and Prof had to go to bed early every night for a year.

'I'm never going to invent anything ever again,' Freddie said, 'people just don't understand us scientists.'

FOCUS QUESTIONS

1   Why is the homework machine a failure?

2   Give a number of reasons why Freddie decides to build a shopping machine for his mother.

3   Give some reasons why Freddie and Prof are such good friends.

4   In what respects is it suggested that Prof's mother and Freddie's mother are very much alike?

5   Why does it take Prof and Freddie so long to draw up their plans and then test the shopping machine?

6   Why is Prof's mother worried about the boys' plans to test the new machine in the garage?

7   In what respects does the machine look like a human being?

8   How does Freddie's mother react when she hears about what has happened at Mr Grumpy's?

9   Why does the supermarket manager ring the fire brigade?

10 Do you think that Freddie and Prof are punished either too harshly or too leniently?

EXPLORING WORDS

11 Match each of the following words from the story with its appropriate meaning in the second column.

Words from the story

a   'He made some <u>adjustments</u> to the machine.'
b   '. . . Freddie's mother <u>slumped</u> into a chair, exhausted.'
c   'They [the plans] were very <u>complicated</u>.'
d   'Freddie felt <u>nervous</u>.'
e   'A <u>nasty</u> dog heard it coming.'
f   '. . . the let dog out a loud <u>yelp</u>.'
g   'He stared with wide eyes as the <u>strange</u> machine came into his shop.'
h   '"Thank you," the machine said <u>gruffly</u>.'

i '... Freddie and Prof <u>pestered</u> her.'

j '"We're being <u>invaded</u> by robots," a woman yelled.'

Meanings

Difficult.
A quick, sharp bark.
Attacked.
Harshly.
Unfriendly.
Modifications.
Uneasy.
Unusual.
Annoyed.

WRITING

12 You encourage Freddie to change his mind and he finally agrees to your request to invent another machine. You decide what it will be and draw up the detailed plans or clearly labelled illustrations to assist him. Describe what happens after the machine has been built.

S. H. C.

hen Mrs Hopkins left to have a baby, One Set Two had a new teacher for English. The new teacher was soft and did a lot of grinning. You could tell her *anything*. They called her Smiler. She smiled on and on, even when they made a racket. One Set Two thought she wasn't quite right in the head.

On this particular morning, the boys came charging into Smiler's room before the girls, hot-foot from Registration. Some pulled up abruptly as they crashed across the threshold, as if an invisible rider had yanked hard on an imaginary rein. They looked across at Smiler. But she never said, 'Go out and form a line and do it *properly* this time.' She just smiled on.

'Miss, Miss!' yelled Gary Radford, flapping the air with *Adventures in Science*, Issue One. He was building it up into an encyclopedia. 'Will you read us a bit out of this? It's dead good – all about S.H.C.'

'S.H.C.?' smiled Smiler, raising an eyebrow and scratching her nose. 'What's S.H.C.?'

'Spontaneous Human Combustion. It says this man went up in flames when he was just sitting on the *bog*. It says it's caused by stress.'

The girls, who didn't charge through the door but appeared to sleepwalk in, leaning at an angle of forty-five degrees to the door jambs and one another, groaned heavily. 'Aw, Miss. Don't let them get on to S.H.C. It takes for ever.'

Three others had joined Gary, clamouring round Miss at the table, jabbing well-chewed fingers at the pictures. 'Look at *this*, Miss. Isn't it 'orrible?' 'Go on, read it, Miss.' 'Yeah, Miss! I've got this book all about S.H.C. at home, Miss. I'll bring it in tomorrer.'

'Mrs Walker!' A tall thin figure at the door. All eyes swivelled to it. The Deputy Headmistress, quivering like a compass needle.

'I don't think One Set Two has time to waste being read to, Mrs Walker. One Set Two cannot spell "cuneiform". They cannot spell "Tutankhamun". One Set Two cannot even spell "pyramid" or "papyrus".' Flecks of spit flew before Mrs Cuthbert's words and she scanned the class, like a ship's beam, for gigglers. 'I thought, Mrs Walker, that you might outline the story of Antony and Cleopatra for them this morning. To assist them with their History. I am all in favour, One Set Two, of an integrated curriculum.' And with that she cruised off.

One Set Two looked a little stunned. 'She's all in favour of a what-er?' asked Barbara Heyward.

'Summat to do with curry, weren't it?' said David Wheeler. 'Must be a Paki-lover.'

'Shurrup, you,' growled Baljit Singh, shoving David.

'Shurrup, yourself, Sing-a-Song-Of-Sixpence,' said David, snatching Baljit's rubber and flicking it across to Peter Kilbourne who fielded it neatly.

'Mrs Cuthbert dictates History that fast,' grumbled Sharon Perkins, 'me arm feels like it's gonna drop off.'

'Well now,' said Mrs Walker, hitching her skirt and sitting on the edge of the table. 'Antony and Cleopatra. Cleopatra was an adventurous lady. She was once delivered to a man rolled up in a carpet.'

One Set Two punched one another in delight and giggled and whispered behind their hands and settled down.

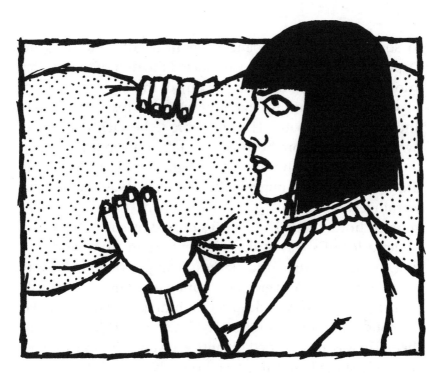

'Can we act it, Miss?' said Julie Hill who fancied being Cleopatra.

'Yeah,' said David Wheeler, turning his head till his nose was parallel with his shoulder and talking out of the side of his mouth. 'And you can be the carpet, baby.'

'Cleopatra put an asp to her busom,' wrote Gary Radford that evening in the exercise book he used for a diary. 'An asp is a venomous serpent. She must've got *sucked* to death.' Gary looked thoughtfully at what he'd just written. This week he was practising writing very, very small. He was currently averaging twenty-two words to the line. The Deputy Head had written, 'This is the work of a demented ant', in big letters across his History book. He looked back at last week's entries. Last week he'd been into topping his 'i's and 'j's with little circles instead of dots, and the Deputy Head had written, 'Stop this affectation', and the week before that he'd done great looping 'g's and 'y's, heavy as pears, drooping on to the line below. He didn't have room for the words and had to squash them all up and even he'd got confused. The Deputy Head had written, 'Contracted the dropsy?' He didn't know what she was on about in any of them.

Gary turned his thoughts away from his handwriting and back to Cleopatra. How horrible to be sucked to death by a snake! No more horrible, though, than spontaneously to combust. Gary shifted in his chair and began to tear at the skin round his fingers with his teeth. Was there some warning when it was going to happen? Could you feel yourself hotting up? They say it's caused by stress. Gary was under a lot of stress at the moment. Apart from worrying that he might burst into flames at any moment, he was worried that Mrs Walker might not be teaching him English properly. His mam was dead set on him getting O-levels like his cousin Ian. Only another five years and he'd be taking them. He was also worried because everybody in his class had suddenly started fancying everybody else and all he wanted in life was a ferret. He felt very alone. He put a hand to his forehead. Pretty hot. He turned out the electric fire in his bedroom and went across to the bathroom to splash cold water on his face. That should cool him down. He pushed a lot of bottles and packets around in the bathroom cupboard looking for a thermometer. If his temperature was up, he'd take a cold bath . . .

When the boys came tearing into Mrs Walker's room the next day they showed her 'The Beckoning Lady' in *Adventures in Science*. It came under the section 'Apparitions, Poltergeists and E.S.P.' and told how a woman woke one night to see a ghost dressed in grey with an old-fashioned bonnet walk out of her wardrobe and stand by her bed. The ghost didn't *do* anything – just looked down on the woman without smiling. The same thing happened the next night. But the night after that the grey lady crossed to the window and beckoned. 'And I knew then,' said the woman, 'that what she wanted was to entice me to jump to my death.' She had every reason to think so, too, living on the thirty-third floor of a high-rise block. The girls, who loped into the room in the middle of Mrs Walker reading the story, shuddered and clutched each other. All except Julie Hill who was stuck in the doorway between a suitcase and what looked like a large roll of carpet.

'I had this dream once,' said Gary in a low voice to Mrs Walker as she waved the rest of the class to their places, 'that I was looking at my own tombstone.' He said it low because in point of fact he'd seen it on 'Strange Tales' on the telly. He didn't suppose Mrs Walker ever watched 'Strange Tales'. All teachers watch is the Last Night of the Proms and Party Political Broadcasts.

'Tutankhamun,' said Mrs Walker when at last they had settled down and were still, 'was a king and he died very young.' Gary began to feel himself hotting up. 'He married a child bride.' Gary felt himself getting yet hotter. 'The two of them were not much older than you lot. When he died he was only in his teens and they buried him in the Valley of the Kings. In a tomb of gold within a room of gold, with a gold chariot, and a death mask of gold upon his face. Can you imagine what it was like when they found the entrance to the tomb, only this century, and room after golden room?' One Set Two stirred. 'On top of his tomb,' said Mrs Walker, 'his bride placed a garland of flowers. Think how sad she must have been. The tomb was sealed up and the air was so still that the flowers remained intact for over three thousand years. But when they opened up the chamber, the air got in and the flowers just crumbled into dust.' One Set Two sighed and were still.

'Can we do Cleopatra now, Miss?' asked Julie Hill at last. 'I've brought a bit of carpet in, Miss,' and she yanked up the roll from the gangway to show Mrs Walker.

'All right,' said Mrs Walker, 'but just let's go over the story once again. If you remember, Antony was Cleopatra's boyfriend much later than the carpet incident. Who was

Cleopatra's boyfriend earlier on, when she was delivered all rolled up?'

Gary's hand shot up. A look of intense pain came over his face, as he gripped his armpit with his other hand and flicked from the wrist as if he wanted shut of his fingers for ever. 'Miss. Oooh, Miss.'

'Yes, Gary.'

'Caesar, Miss,' said Gary crisply, looking triumphantly round at the others as if expecting a standing ovation. Julie Hill pulled her eyes down at the corners at him till the reds showed.

'Quite right, Gary,' said Mrs Walker, 'and since you show such enthusiasm, I think you should play the part of Caesar, don't you?'

The class cheered and Gary buckled up. '*Oh, no*, Miss. Please.' Julie Hill squealed in distress, rolled down her lower lip and dashed her face into her hands, but very soon recovered. 'I've brought a costume as well, Miss,' she said, hoisting up the suitcase. 'Can I go to the toilets to change?'

Mrs Walker gave permission and Julie, hardly able to believe her luck, said quickly, 'Can Sharon come too, Miss, to help me get ready?' She stuck up both thumbs and nodded her head very fast at her friend like a chicken pecking corn. The two of them dashed out, leaving the class to dream up suitable clothing for Imperial Caesar.

Fifteen minutes later Julie and Sharon returned, bent double with laughing, holding one another up. Cleopatra wore her coat clutched round her middle like a dressing-gown and from underneath floated a lot of shocking pink net. Her eyes had been alarmingly extended towards her eyebrows with bat wings of blue paint and edged with wiggly black lines. Her lips were plastered thick as raspberry jam on toast. She wore a gold head-band slung low across her brow from which sprouted a peacock feather so long it bent as she entered the door. Across her forehead, cheeks and chin she had stuck pink and purple sequins and she jangled at the wrist and ankle with lines and lines of bracelets, and row upon row of beads clinked against the studs of what looked like a dog-collar round her neck. She waded into the room on four-inch stiletto mules.

Four handmaidens and four carpet-bearers were sent off to wrap up the human parcel and at last the carpet was carried shoulder high from the jumping horse just outside the door with Julie Hill ceremonially rolled up inside it. Or, rather, her head and body were rolled up but her legs stuck out at the other end like a mummified clothes-peg. With a jerk and a bump the package was placed on the ground at the feet of Imperial Caesar who wore five tea towels borrowed from the Home Economics block for a toga. Two round his legs, two round his body and one draped becomingly over one shoulder. On his head he wore a crown of wire with a few browning ivy leaves growing out of it. Baljit Singh, who was the carpet-seller, said, 'I have a fine piece from the East for your delight, O Caesar,' and with a flourish unrolled the carpet with his foot. Up jumped Julie Hill, hair and eyes wild, cheeks

red as crab-apples, and Caesar the Great choked and clutched himself with horror as a great wave of blistering heat broke over him at the sight of her, and the Deputy Head walked in.

What the Deputy Head saw was One Set Two jumping up and down in the gangways, One Set Two kneeling on desks, One Set Two gasping for breath and clinging on to one another and generally falling about. That terrible Julie Hill was leaping up like a Hollywood star out of a birthday cake, wearing what looked like her mother's négligée and an awful lot of jewellery and little else besides. And Gary Radford was dressed entirely in tea towels with *ivy leaves* in his hair and was clearly over-excited.

'*Mrs Walker!*' bellowed the Deputy Head. All eyes rushed to her, iron filings to a magnet. 'Can I have a word with you, please, *outside*.' Gary completely forgot that he was about to combust spontaneously in the delighted realisation that if anybody was going to, it would be the Deputy Head. She was as blotchy as salami and turning purple fast.

But when the Deputy Head returned five minutes later there was no sign of scorch marks, worse luck. She rapidly put an end to five glorious minutes during which One Set Two had run entirely amok. Cleopatra had married Caesar under a deluge of English exercise-book confetti and the happy couple were still sparkle-eyed and clutching hands. Four more girls had laid claim to four more boys by leaping out at them from a series of carpet packages and there was just about to be a mass wedding and another great confetti storm when the Deputy Head walked in for the second time.

Slowly, very slowly, like those suffering from hangovers after the most tremendous night on the town, One Set Two gathered up every scrap of confetti. The Deputy Head yanked Julie off to the cloakroom and personally supervised, arms crossed, while she scrubbed off every bit of the bat wings and the raspberry jam. Then she confiscated the magic carpet. 'Mrs Walker will no longer be taking you for English, One Set Two,' concluded the Deputy Head. 'I shall take that little responsibility entirely upon my own shoulders and from now on this period on a Friday will be given up entirely to a *Spelling Test!'*

But Gary hardly heard. Since he hadn't spontaneously combusted, that searing blast of heat could mean only one thing. *He actually fancied Julie Hill and he wasn't a freak after all.* And she'd married him in the face of Mrs Walker and an entire congregation.

Julie and Gary sat on the wall by the bus stop after school with their arms round one another. Gary didn't remove his arm even when Mrs Walker grinned into view. He looked at her curiously instead for any signs of albino rabbit pink eyes but she didn't look in the slightest put out. In fact she just carried straight on grinning. 'Have a good weekend, both of you,' she said, 'and don't go up in smoke.'

Gary grinned politely at her. 'No, we won't,' he said, and pulled Julie off the wall, keeping hold of her hand and whistling, as the bus came. No danger of that any longer, now he felt so grown-up and cool. He wasn't under any stress now, either, since they wouldn't be having Smiler for English. He was really glad about that. What with having the Deputy Head for Spelling every Friday, a whole galaxy of O-levels was positively guaranteed. He'd show his mam. He'd do just as good at school as his cousin Ian. And no sweat.

FOCUS QUESTIONS

1   Explain in simple terms the meaning of the phrase 'Spontaneous Human Combustion'.

2   In general, what are the differences in attitude and behaviour between the boys and girls in One Set Two?

3   What is Smiler's real name?

4   What is the name of the Deputy Headmistress?

5   What does the Deputy teach?

6   What does the Deputy mean when she says she is in favour of an 'integrated curriculum'?

7   Why does David call Baljit 'Sing-a-Song-of-Sixpence'?

8   Explain what the Deputy Head meant in each case when she wrote:
    a 'This is the work of a demented ant'.
    b 'Stop this affectation'.
    c 'Contracted the dropsy?'

9   Gary believed that S.H.C. was caused by stress. Make a list of all the things Gary was worried about at this time.

10 Why was Gary (as Caesar the Great) so overcome when Julie (as Cleopatra) was unrolled from the carpet at his feet?

EXPLORING WORDS

11 Arrange the following words from the story in alphabetical order and then use your dictionary to find their meanings.

Racket	Entice
Cuneiform	Ovation
Extrasensory perception (E.S.P.)	Sequins
Adventurous	Imperial
Thermometer	Flourish
Apparition	

WRITING

12 As a parent, write a letter to the head of the school, either supporting or opposing the Deputy's decision to replace Mrs Walker as One Set Two's English teacher.

13 Similes are comparisons that use 'like' or 'as' to compare two different things. They are used to add interest to writing, and to help us gain a picture of what is being described. Make a list of all the similes you can find in this story. For example:

▶ 'Some pulled up . . . as if an invisible rider had yanked hard on an imaginary rein.'

▶ The Deputy Headmistress, quivering like a compass needle.'

There are at least four other examples of similes in the story.

Who Wins, Zadig?

I t isn't as easy as you think being a teacher – being in charge of kids. In an average day I face two hundred and ten different kids over seven periods. Two hundred and ten different faces looking up at you and expecting something. Can you imagine that! I tell you it can be a grind. And my good nature gets me into all kinds of difficult situations with my two hundred and ten kids a day. Like last week.

I was running late for school. Again. This time it was a genuine reason. I mean it's always a genuine reason but this one was, shall we say, substantially genuine. Beyond my control. My car broke down on Parramatta Road. You can imagine how embarrassing that was. Had to get a tow truck. And then the Head saw me tip-toeing down the corridor late to my first English class. How annoying! And then when I got into class I remembered I had promised faithfully to phone somebody, to leave my class first thing to phone someone who'd be waiting by her phone – my mother, actually.

Oh well, I may as well tell you – it wasn't my mother at all. It was a woman. I'd met her at a teachers' meeting the night before. Actually the most interesting teachers' meeting I've ever attended. I've forgotten quite what it was about but Irena, this teacher I met, well – you know how these things happen. And I'd promised, solemnly promised to phone Irena at her school

in first period. She said when I did she'd know I really wanted
to see her again. She wasn't teaching first period – was I? Uh no,
I said and then she said, Good – well then maybe we could
arrange about dinner that night. That is, if I wanted to arrange
about dinner. Naturally I did.

So I said to my class – a nice mature group of kids with
only a few meat-heads in it, that they could do a writing
assignment for me while I had an important meeting. (I know
it wasn't exactly a meeting but it was important.) They could
write a description – yes that's it – a description of their room.

They all groaned. It's kind of tradition to groan. They always
do, whenever I say we'll write anything. So I didn't react. But
Josephine Hill, my best writer said 'My Room?', so disgustedly;
and Dimitri Cadzos, such a nice kid, sighed so audibly; and
the rest of them were slumped so dully in their chairs that I
said, just off the cuff (that's the way it happens – these things
come to me just like that – ways to get kids involved – which I
like to do even when I don't have important phone calls to
make), anyway, quick as a flash I said, 'But this is no ordinary
assignment. This is a special assignment. An assignment
extraordinaire. It's a competition. To see who can write the most
unusual, the most gripping, the most original description of
his or her room.'

'You mean weird or something?' Mark Robins asked.

'If that's what you want to do, Mark, something weird.'

'You win something?' Selina asked.

'Sure,' I said trying to think if I still had any crisp new
copies of *A Tale of Two Cities*. I'd bought a box at a church fete
with the idea of class prizes.

'Not a book I hope,' Josephine likes her little jokes.

'Nah – sir's got something heaps better for the prize, haven't
you sir?' Deidre Flanagan asked.

'What *is* the prize, Mr Zadig? Sir?' Dimitri asked. Class interest
seemed high at this moment. Everyone looking my way.
Everyone eager. And as luck would have it the Head walked
past just at this moment. He smiled in at the intent class and

the talented, compelling teacher hard at work with the thirty spellbound young ones and then he swept by. On his way to the deputy's office no doubt for his usual morning-long meeting. Now was the chance to slip into the staff room and phone Irena.

But I must keep their little heads down – all thirty little heads. I could see Kate Murphy was already losing interest, jabbing at her girlfriend with a pencil.

'Ahh, the prize is . . .' I was groping for an idea. I had discarded the idea of the crisp new books for the moment.

'Money, I hope,' Shane Peters stage whispered. I wouldn't have thought of it otherwise. But what with time ticking on and Irena waiting . . .

'Yes, Shane. Quite right, ten dollars for the lucky person to write the most original story.'

'Yeah? Ten dollars! Wow!'

'Great.'

They were clearly enthusiastic about their task and began writing at once. Before I left the room, a scene of complete industry, I said 'But it musn't be over two pages long.' I wasn't

going to fall for the old mark-thirty-long-assignments-trick. No way. I have better things to do with my evenings especially with Irena on the scene. 'Short and sweet,' I said as I left the room thinking of Irena, 'and different!'

I came back from my phone call smiling. A lot of the kids were still working and I had to wrench some of the assignments from them. 'Next week, same class, I'll announce the competition winner,' I promised.

I couldn't do it till then because it was payday next week.

'I bet Josephine Hill wins it,' someone said as they left the room.

As luck would have it I had a spare period next and sat down to tackle the *My Room* assignments straight away. Now this is the part I was talking about before – when I said my good nature often gets me into trouble. Every single one of those assignments was good. Far from being boring or dreary, as some of my marking can be at times, I sat for the next forty minutes quite delighted. Yes, the stories were good all right! Each one stranger, it seemed to me, than the one before. Weird and/or wonderful as pupil outdid pupil. Some were more than two pages and I didn't mind at all. By the time I'd finished reading, I realised that probably every kid in the class deserved ten dollars! Talk about original! Of course I realised that they had had the benefit of a superior teacher for more than six months. Such originality. Such style.

But thirty times ten dollars by anyone's maths is $300! Not much less than I took home for a week's work! And I had the rent and the broken down car . . . and now my date with Irena to think of.

How would I choose? I thought of asking Irena to help me but I didn't want her to get the idea that I was a workaholic or anything. So I stewed over the best twenty of those thirty assignments for three or four days. $200 was too much, way too much to pay out if I chose the best twenty. Get on with it, Zadig. Be brutal. Make your choice. You're a teacher of great talent, great discernment. You can do it! Who wins, Zadig?

Unwillingly I isolated the best ten. Then I agonised. Ten really original stories. $100? Ridiculous. I said I'd choose the best. I took myself well in hand, re-read my favourite ten and threw out six more.

Down to four now. But those four stories burned in my brain. How to choose one and do it fairly? I agonised for another two days but with Monday coming up I knew I had to do it. OK, OK. I threw out another two. There, I'd almost done it! Two quite amazing stories left.

The interesting thing was that the two I finally considered the most originally written were by kids who, though they always wrote quite well, had never done anything remarkable in their assignments before.

Marty is a quiet boy who sits right at the back, he works well enough but never says boo to a goose. And Deidre is a bit of a pain who sits right at the front and generally twists her hair as she secretly reads her way through all my lessons. I shouldn't complain. The book I took from her last week was *War and Peace* (or was it *War and Peas*?). Maybe a bit more interesting than what I was telling the kids about the subjunctive.

Now it was between the two of them. Who would it be? Marty or Deidre? Deidre or Marty?

Well that's where I'm up to. You could say give two prizes but after all I said I'd choose the best *one*. And that's what I'm going to do. Easier said than done of course.

In desperation I've put the two stories side by side right here. See which one you think should win, if you can . . .

My Room by Marty Mason

It's not a very big room and it's cluttered with furniture. A bed of course which runs lengthwise by the window. A pine chest of drawers with two of the drawers broken. An old fashioned wardrobe made of very solid wood with detailed brass handles and a little crest of carved wood at the top for decoration. A full-length mirror is on the inside of the door which is annoyingly hanging open because of a faulty hinge and/or the force of

gravity. There's a chair that used to be in the lounge room until the springs went. It's covered with clothing and if you dig deeply enough you could work out what I wore last Saturday.

A desk that is littered with things. Seven or eight exercise books; assorted text books; a hand calculator – old fashioned; a tin with several stumps of pencils and four pens – two green, one red and one black; an orange peel – fairly recent; a photo frame with Don Bradman in it, and another photo frame with my grandfather holding my father (naturally my father was a baby at the time). There is a picture on the wall by Escher showing a seated man offering a crystal in which the whole of the room is depicted. His hand is awkwardly large and the room is circular, contained in the crystal.

So that's about it, you might say. That's my room. But sometimes when I'm lying in my bed I think, But this room goes on forever. There's what hits you in the eye, the things I've described. And then there's what's hidden, covered over, like my last Saturday's clothes.

Begin with the carpet, an old fashioned swirly grey carpet, mostly very dirty – sand from my beach towel, a few fleas hopping about and plenty of dust because I only vacuum when Mum schitzes like mad about it. But lying in my bed, I picture what's beneath the dusty, swirly, grey carpet. Wide floorboards (it's an old house) – boards not seen for years – at least twenty years. They'd be pale and smooth – like Josephine Hill's legs when she gets into swimmers. Pale, pale and smooth. Naked floorboards.

Nails in straight lines in the boards – old nails, too, but unchanged. Firmly pressing the boards to the crossbeams. The underside of the boards would not be pale and smooth though. They'd be hung with cobwebs, spattered with mildew, spotted with the slow filter of years of dust that has found its way between my floorboards.

And below them earth. Not like in the backyard that's covered in grass – no, a dampish, dank, stinking earth where no light comes – cockroaches, mice, rats and the sour detritus of their droppings. Who knows what lurks here? The smell is old, stale and still. It is the beginning of death. Yes, that's what I imagine as I lie in my bed on the dusty, swirly, grey carpet. The going-downness of my room below the floorboards to the first layer of the earth. And then down, down again, beneath the earth.

Blind worms and other wriggling creeping mites move about darkly in the slim layer of the damp earth. They burrow, crawl, twist and loop their way, these sightless creatures, through a slimy soil.

But go deeper, down deeper where it is still and quiet. No creatures in that airless dark place. Only water that finds its way from the surface, can seep and seep finding its way there. Down there. Down deep. Here's where you'll find the first bones. Bones of what had once lived on the surface. Wallabies or kangaroos that may have grazed. Or the first people. Yes, skulls maybe of who knows who and those other bony remains of living things. Down there deep, down below my room. They are anchored in packed soil, compressed but preserved in that still stratum that's under my bed.

And keep going, beneath that layer again. I see the vastness of dark open space then. Limestone caves. Great yawning caverns honeycombing the under earth – a great hanging void beneath my bed.

Fall through it and presto you're really moving way, way down there now. Into the serious business. On towards the core. Down into the magma, the molten rock beneath the solid crust. Magma, mantle, core! No 'living things' lurk here.

Deeper, through the crevasses and cracks and fissures, the promise of what's to come. Not the scorching or charring or singeing – that's already done. No, into the violent, spuming red, the vitreolic furnace of the molten mass. Right to the centre that constitutes a living core, the very innards of planet Earth. Right into the breathless heated holocaust. Then what? You can't go any further than the heart.

Yes, that's how I sometimes see my room.

My Room by Deidre Flanagan

My room had no treasure in it until last Thursday night. My room is pretty tatty with a broken bedhead (Mum means to mend it but doesn't), a broken venetian blind (that lets in the light too early in the morning) and my sister who scatters things from one end of the place to the other. But now, since last Thursday, it has a treasure. I've made a special place on the table where I do my homework – that is, *when* I do my homework – for this treasure. Let me tell you about it.

An object. Small, scrolled silver with a fine hinge. Cool to hold in your hand or press against your hot cheek. Lovely, lovely to look at. Yes, this object is beautiful to look at but it is especially beautiful because it has saved lives. How could a silver scrolled object small enough to hold in your hand save lives, you ask? Well, remember the story of the mouse and the lion?

My grandfather came to visit last Thursday night and he gave gifts to my sister Nellie and to me. He gave Nellie an old silver hairbrush that had been Grandma's. She was really

pleased with it and I think she was a bit sorry for me with my gift – the silver scrolled object small enough to fit in my hand. But I liked it very much, my gift. And when Nellie had gone off with her boyfriend to the movies, my grandfather told me a story that made me like it even more.

Once, when he was a boy, his dad Alex had been the best fisherman on Blackhead Beach. Blackhead was a simple village in those days. My great-grandfather Alex built a house there with his own hands and the family stayed by the sea all summer and Alex went fishing, often alone.

There was a smart young man came down from the city of Brisbane to holiday. He only had a few days at Blackhead Beach. He told Alex that he was determined to go fishing if he could just find someone to take him out. There was nothing, he told Alex, that he didn't know about fishing and he even had a mind to go out night fishing. Alex didn't like the man's swaggering manner but he hung around, this Danny, and nagged until Alex finally agreed to take him out in his boat.

They fished the afternoon away with Danny getting madder and madder as Alex made his usual haul. Late afternoon, gazing at the horizon and at the nature of the tides coming in, Alex was all for pulling up anchor. 'There'll be a storm for sure,' he told Danny. But Danny was angry at having caught very few fish. 'I'm paying you well and you agreed to six hours.'

'You can take back your money – all of it. I'm not staying out here in a row boat in any storm.'

'Well, just another half-hour then,' Danny wheedled.

'It'll be hard going to get back in if we wait another half-hour, I promise you.'

'Scared of water are you?'

'Respectful,' Alex answered, unruffled.

Of course Alex was right in his predictions. A storm blew up within half-an-hour and there was a terrible struggle to bring the little boat in. It veered off near the headland in a raging wind and carried them towards deserted Redhead Beach. But short of the surf the boat overturned and filled and went

down in a matter of minutes. Now Alex was a fisherman and a swimmer but Danny, as it turned out, was neither. He clung to Alex and it was all Alex could do to drag the heavy fellow through a wild surf. There was a moment when Alex lost him and Danny was submerged for minutes. But somehow Alex, who was as determined as he was strong, found the inert body and dragged it through the waves and onto the beach at Redhead.

They were a long way from home, exposed to driving rain and Danny was only half conscious. Alex was cold and exhausted but he realised that his unwelcome fishing mate would surely die if left on the beach in the rain. Alex was a practical man. He saw what needed to be done and set about doing it. Within minutes he'd found a shelter under a ledge of rock for Danny who now lay shivering and moaning. He collected driftwood and the brittle bushes growing amongst scattered rocks and made a neat pile against the cliff face.

And then he took from his sodden shirt pocket a small shining object made of scrolled silver that had a hinged top. It sprung open and revealed tinder dry matches inside. Enough of them to light an unwilling sputtering fire that turned slowly, slowly into a healthy, warming fire and that finally blazed with a heat that breathed life back into Danny's frozen body and warmed Alex through as he fed the fire the whole night long.

Next morning they were found by neighbours who came by boat through a startlingly calm sea looking for them.

'Storm stopped you two last night!' they said coming ashore.

'Thank God for this lighter, lads!' Alex told them. 'This lighter was a real life saver.'

'Tough time of it, eh?' they asked.

'Oh, nothing we couldn't handle,' Danny blathered.

You see some people don't know when to be humble or when to be thankful. They simply never learn.

Grandad said when he offered me the gift, 'My father, Alex, gave me this silver match case as I'm giving it to you. And he added, "Treasure it, because it saved two men's lives. And one of them was forever grateful".'

My room had no treasure in it until last Thursday night.

Deidre or Marty? Marty or Deidre? Who wins, Zadig? Who?

FOCUS QUESTIONS

1 Why does Mr Zadig frequently find himself in difficult situations?

2 Why is he late for school?

3 What prompts Mr Zadig to set a writing task for his class?

4 How does the class react to Mr Zadig's suggestion that the topic is to be 'My Room'?

5 Why does Mr Zadig offer ten dollars to the person who writes the most original story? What do you think about his offer?

6 What is the dilemma Mr Zadig faces when he has read all thirty assignments for the first time?

7 What is surprising about the two assignments that Mr Zadig eventually selects as the potential winner?

8 Make a brief summary of what Marty Mason's story tells you about himself and his family.

EXPLORING WORDS

9 Look at each set of three words in the **Words** column and choose the best word in each set that matches the meaning in the **Meanings** column.

Words	**Meanings**
a Imagine / Arrange / Agonise	Unusual.
b Difficult / Genuine / Solemn	Serious.
c Fissure / Holocaust / Void	An empty space.
d Faithfully / Disgustedly / Audibly	Loyally.
e Talented / Inert / Deserted	Inactive.
f Exhausted / Determined / Cluttered	Drained.
g Embarrassed / Annoyed / Amazed	Astonished.
h Veered / Scrolled / Stewed	Changed direction.
i Spattered / Unruffled / Spellbound	Entranced.
j Molten / Weird / Mature	Strange.

WRITING AND DISCUSSION

10 In your opinion, who deserves to win? Write down a list of reasons to support your point of view.

11 Who do you think Mr Zadig will choose to be the winner? Give reasons as to why or why not you think he may agree with your choice.

A Family Affair

Robbo's Fair was in trouble. The Robinson family had owned and worked in their travelling fair for thirty-five years. At one time there had been more than forty Robinsons employed by the fair. Now there were sixteen, and if the fair didn't start drawing bigger crowds soon, there wouldn't be any: the fair would have to close.

A family meeting was called after a very unsuccessful three days at Stroud. Grandpa Arthur, who had inherited the fair from his father, twenty-five years ago, squashed all sixteen Robinsons into Aunty Coreen's fortune-telling caravan.

'We don't need Aunty Coreen to tell us our fortune, if we don't start drawing more customers,' he said. 'We need something new, something different.'

'No, we don't,' said his brother Jack, who was now too old to even ride the dodgem cars. He switched the power on and off in the box.

'Oh, shut up, Jack,' said Arthur. 'We all know what you want. It's no good having the fat lady, the bearded lady, or even Indian knife-throwers. They're out of date.'

'If we fed Martha up, she could be the fattest lady ever,' said Jack. 'I mean, look at her, she nearly fills this caravan herself.'

'I don't want to be fat,' wailed Martha.

'You've got to do your bit for the family,' said Jack.

'Even if people would look at fat or bearded ladies,' said Jack, 'there would be a crowd of women's-libbers and doctors, and goodness knows *who* all, after us. They'd say we were exploiting people.'

'Wall of Death,' shouted young Vincent, who fancied his chances on a motorbike.

'Kids' stuff. They've seen better things on telly,' said Arthur.

'Three-headed sheep,' suggested Aunty Ida. 'I can still sew heads on so they wouldn't notice.'

'RSPCA would get you,' said Arthur. 'In any case, people aren't as simple as they used to be. They need sensational things.'

'Maybe we should set fire to ourselves,' said Jack bitterly. 'They'd turn up to watch that.'

'You could only do it once, Jack,' laughed Arthur.

'I've got an idea,' said Grandma Vera.

They listened and shook their heads, but in the end Arthur decided to let her try.

People were still thin on the ground when the family fair moved to Buckingham. At nine o'clock on the Monday evening there was only one queue – for the Big Wheel. John and Stuart Robinson kept the rides as short as they dared; they knew the profits they made were vital to the fair.

'Next,' called John, and two small boys rushed to the seat that had reached the bottom.

'Hey, wait for the old lady to get out,' said Stuart.

'She's gone to sleep. Can't be a very frightening Big Wheel,' sneered one of the boys.

'Stand back, all of you,' said John urgently.

The old lady had her mouth open and was slumped right back.

'She's dead,' whispered someone near the front of the queue.

The queue watched in silence as the old lady was carried away by Edna and Geraldine, who were in charge of the nearby candyfloss stall.

'We're sorry about that,' said John to the queue. 'We want to warn everybody that this is one of the most frightening Big Wheels in the country. We do get people fainting.'

'*Fainting*? She's *dead*,' said a fat man in a blue mac. John pretended to look sheepish.

'Well, if she's had a heart-attack it is understandable,' he said. 'I'm afraid I'll have to ask anybody who is of a nervous disposition to go away. We don't want another accident.'

Stuart had made an 'Out of Order' sign. He put it on the dead lady's seat.

Nobody went away. In fact the queue grew longer. As the news of the death spread, people came to gawp at the 'Out of Order' seat and stayed to have a ride. They all agreed it was a very scary Big Wheel.

Next day there was a bigger crowd. When the fair left town the takings were up. People had heard about the terrifying Big Wheel and wanted to try it themselves. Of course, once they were there they spent their money on other things.

The Robinsons had another meeting the night before they were due in Stratford.

'Told you it would work,' said Grandma Vera, triumphantly.

'Well done, or rather well died, Vera,' said Arthur. 'But you can't die everywhere. I mean word will spread. I bet some of them are already wondering why there was no report of your death in the local paper.'

'I'll die again in Grantham,' said Vera. 'That place needs livening up.'

Grandma Vera died on the dodgems in Grantham and, a fortnight later, moaned and dropped dead on the cake-walk in Hull. It was on the Big Wheel again in Newcastle that she was caught. Edna and Geraldine were carrying her off dead when Edna bumped into Aunty Coreen's caravan and let Gran's head slip and bump on the pavement. Grandma rose from the dead in a rage.

'You clumsy fool, our Edna,' yelled Gran. 'You might have killed me.'

'It's a trick,' a thin man with black eyes shouted to the rest of the crowd who were watching the corpse being carried away. 'She's perfectly all right, and what's more they know each other.'

The police were called. Arthur Robinson told them the whole story.

'It's not against the law,' said Arthur. 'What law have we broken?'

'Well, it's fraud really,' said the policeman, but he looked doubtful.

'Fraud means cheating people out of money. We haven't done that.'

'Well, in a way you have . . . look, I'll let you off with a warning, but don't do it again.'

Next week in Berwick takings were low again. Grandma Vera, recovered from her bumped head, went to see Arthur.

'You can't do it again. It's fraud,' said Arthur.

'Not if you tell 'em I'm going to die,' said Grandma.

A fortnight later the Robinsons' Fair came to Carlisle. The publicity posters contained a new item.

'£50 will be paid each night to the person finding the SENSATIONAL DYING GRANDMA.'

It explained how Grandma Vera would be acting dead somewhere in the fair every night.

'She's got to bring in fifty extra people to even make it worth while,' grumbled Jack.

But he changed his mind over the next three days. People turned up in their hundreds to win £50. It was also fun looking for a corpse. Of course you had to have a go on most things, since Grandma was not likely to die on the road or pavement.

At Halifax Grandma lay undetected all night in the pay-box of the Waltzer. At Huddersfield she was found dead slumped over a giant wooden rat in the Chamber of Horrors. Then her act was reported in the newspapers. Wherever the Robinsons went people remembered it was the fair where the old lady did a dying act. They went along to look for her – and stayed to play games and have rides. The Robinson Family Fair was making a profit again.

It was Grandma's over-acting that brought the end. At Barnsley she was found with a scarf round her neck as if throttled. At Wakefield she was found covered in artificial blood. Of course, finding a murdered old lady made it even more exciting.

A small girl at Dewsbury paid for her three hoops. She missed with the first two. Anxious to win a goldfish with the last one she reached over as far as she possibly could. Then she suddenly started to scream – and scream and scream. She had looked down as she reached over and on the floor, up against the boards, she had seen an old lady with a knife stuck in her neck and blood all over the place. The lady's face was ghastly pale – with flour – and her false teeth were sticking out.

Grandma jumped up when she heard the screams and tried to quieten the girl. But even the fifty pounds wouldn't do it. She was hysterical.

'Poor little child,' said someone.

'Oughtn't to be allowed,' said another.

This time the police were more hostile.

'The child could have nightmares for years,' said the Sergeant. 'If we ever hear of you doing it again we'll close your fair.'

So that was the end of Grandma Vera's act. She went back to her old job of counting the takings. But she was still busier than before. The takings stayed up. Long after Grandma's act was banned people said: 'Robinsons. Isn't that the fair that got into trouble because an old lady was murdered there?' And they went along to check up. Grandma Vera had given her life – many times – for the Robinson Fair. But she had not died in vain.

FOCUS QUESTIONS

1 Why is the Robinsons' fair in danger of closing?

2 Reconsider each of the various suggestions made by family members to save the fair. Say whether or not you agree with their reasons for rejecting them in favour of Grandma Vera's plan.

3 What is Grandma Vera's plan?

4 Why do John and Stuart keep rides on the Big Wheel 'as short as they dared'?

5 What attracts more customers to take rides on the Big Wheel?

6 Do you think the Robinsons are actually committing fraud, that is, deliberately deceiving people, especially for unlawful or unfair gain?

7 What is Grandma Vera's next plan?

8 Explain the meaning of the following sentences:
   a 'It was Grandma's over-acting that brought the end.'
   b 'Grandma Vera had given her life – many times – for the Robinson Fair. But she had not died in vain.'

WRITING AND DISCUSSION

9 Imagine that Grandma Vera comes out of retirement to do one final performance. What happens?

10 Write down or present an oral account of your most memorable experiences at a carnival or show. For example, an exhilarating or scary ride, being swindled, or winning first prize.

11 Write some brief character sketches of some interesting people you are likely to see, or have seen, at carnivals, fairs and shows.

Barker

There was a rich old woman called Mrs Barker who lived in a pokey little house at the top of a street so steep that it had steps instead of pavements. Mrs Barker could look all the way down the street from her windows and watch people puffing up the steps to bring her presents. Quite a lot of people did that, because Mrs Barker didn't have any sons or daughters or nieces or nephews, only what she called 'sort-ofs'. Sort-of-nieces, sort-of-nephews, sort-of-cousins and so on.

You want an example? Mr Cyril Blounder's mother's father's father's mother's sister had married Mrs Barker's father's mother's brother. That made Mr Blounder a very sort-of sort-of, but it didn't stop him bringing Mrs Barker lettuces from his garden and hoping that one day she'd die and leave him some money in her will. When he came Mrs Barker's maid Hannah would bring him camomile tea, which he pretended to like, while Mrs Barker looked in the lettuces for slugs.

Most of the other sort-ofs did much the same, and they always got given camomile tea, and they all pretended to like it, because of the will. When they left, Mrs Barker would stand at her window and watch them go muttering down the hill. *She* knew what they were thinking.

Whenever a new sort-of was born Mrs Barker always sent a silver napkin-ring for a christening present, with a name on it.

She chose the name herself, without asking the parents, so that was what the child got called. The parents usually decided it was worth it, because of the will. Mrs Barker preferred what she called 'sensible names'. She wrote them down in the back of her notebook to make sure she didn't choose the same one twice.

After that Mrs Barker paid no attention to the child until it was eight years old. Then she used to send a message inviting it to tea. So the parents would dress the child in its smartest clothes and take it up the steps, reminding it several times on the way to say 'Please' and 'Thank you' and not to make faces when it drank the camomile tea. (Some parents used to give their children camomile tea for a week before the visit, for practice.)

But more important than any of that advice was that when Mrs Barker asked the child what it wanted for a present it must choose something *really worth having*.

Because whatever it wanted, it got.

It was very extraordinary. Mrs Barker wasn't at all generous in other ways. She sent the most miserable mingy presents to the sort-ofs at Christmas, when they all bought her beautiful things they couldn't really afford, but just this once in their lives . . .

She would peer at each child with sharp little eyes and croak in her sour old voice, 'Well, what would you like for a present?' And the child would open its eyes as wide as it could and say a racing-bike *please* or a pony *please* or a huge model railway lay-out *please* . . . Mrs Barker would write the request down in her notebook and put it away, but when the child was gone she would take out the notebook and cross off one of the names in the back.

A few days later the present would come, and it would be the best you could buy – the bike with the most gears, the briskest little pony, the most complicated railway set. But it would be the last good present that child ever got from Mrs Barker.

All this went on for years and years, until there were sort-ofs who'd been to tea with Mrs Barker when *they* were eight, now taking their own children up the steps and telling them to say please and thank you and above all to choose a present *really worth having . . .*

One of these later sort-ofs was called Molly. (Her parents had hoped to call her Claudinetta, but it said Molly on her ring.) She was taken up the steps wearing a pink bow in her hair and a pale blue frock with a white lacy apron crackling new, and told all the usual things. Hannah opened the door for her and asked the parents to be back at half past five, and Molly went in alone.

As soon as the door was shut, Molly undid the ribbon in her hair and took off the lacy apron and put them on a chair in the hall before she went into Mrs Barker's parlour and shook hands. Mrs Barker's hand was cold and dry, with loose slithery skin. She pursed her purple lips and peered at Molly.

'You were wearing a pink bow when you came up the steps,' she said.

'I took it off,' said Molly.

Mrs Barker puffed out her cheeks like a frog, but didn't say anything. Hannah brought in the tea, thin little sandwiches, tiny dry cakes and a steaming teapot.

'Do you like camomile tea?' she asked.

'Not much, thank you, but I'll drink it if you want me to.'

Mrs Barker puffed out her cheeks again and peered at Molly, craning her neck like an old tortoise.

'What do you drink at home?' she said.

'Milk. Or orange juice. Or just water.'

Mrs Barker tinkled a small glass bell and when Hannah came she told her to bring Molly a glass of milk. After that they ate tea. Then they played an old-fashioned card-game. Then they did a jigsaw. And then Mrs Barker glanced out of the window and said, 'I can see your father coming up the steps. It is time for you to go. Would you like me to put the bow back in your hair?'

Molly ran and fetched the ribbon and apron and Mrs Barker tied them with trembling old fingers.

'Now,' she said, 'I expect you would like a present.'

Molly had been meaning to ask for a record-player, though she hadn't felt comfortable about it. Her parents had been so eager, so excited about the idea of a present *really worth having*, and now there was something strange in Mrs Barker's dry old voice, as though she was getting herself ready for a disappointment . . .

So without thinking Molly said what she'd felt all along.

'I don't think people should give each other presents till they know each other properly.'

Mrs Barker puffed out her cheeks.

'Very well,' she said.

'Thank you all the same,' said Molly. 'And thank you for the tea.'

Then her father knocked on the door and took her home.

Naturally her family wanted to know what she'd chosen for a present, and when she said nothing they didn't believe her. But nothing came and nothing came and they were furious, while all the other sort-ofs were filled with glee. (None of the sort-of families liked each other much, but that didn't stop them passing the gossip round.)

Then, several weeks later, a message came that Mrs Barker would like Molly to come to tea again, and she was not to dress up specially. This time there were hot buttered scones and fresh chocolate cake and not a whiff of camomile tea anywhere. But nothing was said about presents.

The same thing happened a few weeks later, and a few weeks later still. Now Molly's family was filled with glee and all the other sort-ofs were furious. None of their children had ever been asked to a second tea, so it was obvious Mrs Barker had decided at last who was going to get her money, and now it was too late to tell the children the trick was not to ask the old so-and-so for anything at all.

This went on till almost Christmas, when a letter came.

My dear Molly,

I believe you and I may by now be said to know each other properly, so it is time we exchanged presents. You told me on your last visit that your family dog was about to have puppies. Would you choose one for me, and I shall send you something on Christmas Day.

Yours affectionately,
Ethelswitha Barker

The family dog was a mongrel, and nobody could guess who the father of her last litter might be. Molly's parents wanted to sneak off and buy a beautiful pedigree pup and pretend it came from the litter, but Molly said Mrs Barker was much too sharp not to spot that. She chose a black-and-white male and took it up the hill to show Mrs Barker, who said Molly was to take it home and look after it till it was house-trained. She added that it was to be called Barker. (A sure sign, most of the sort-ofs thought, that she was losing her wits. Naming a dog after your dead husband – honestly!)

Molly's Christmas present turned out to be a yellow water-proof hat and coat and a pair of blue wellies – for taking Barker for walks in wet weather, the note that came with them said.

When he was house-trained Barker went to live with Mrs Barker, and Molly would go most days to take him for a walk. Sometimes she stayed for tea, sometimes not. Time passed. More sort-ofs climbed the hill for their first tea. If they asked for presents they got them, and if they didn't Mrs Barker sent a cheque and note telling the parents to buy something the child needed.

Then people noticed that the writing on the notes was getting shaky. Next they saw the doctor going up the steps to the pokey little house three times in one week. Then an ambulance came. Soon after that Mrs Barker died. All this while Molly took Barker for walks, as usual.

All the sort-ofs were invited to hear the will read. They came, grinding their teeth, except for Molly's parents who did their best not to look too triumphant, though they'd already decided on the grand house outside the town which Molly was going to buy with her money. It had a lovely big garden for her to run about in.

By the time the lawyer had finished reading the will *everybody* was grinding their teeth.

Mrs Barker had left some money to Hannah, enough for her to retire and be comfortable. That wasn't too bad. But then she had left the rest, the whole lot, an enormous amount, to Barker!

And they weren't even going to get their hands on it when Barker died. After that it was going to charity. Until then it was all Barker's. Molly was to be Barker's guardian. There was a lot of legal language, with trustees and heaven knows what, but what it all meant was that Molly was the only person who knew what Barker wanted. If she said Barker was to have something, he was to get it. If not, the money stayed in the bank. And provided Barker lived till Molly was sixteen, she was the one who was going to choose the charities which got the money in the end.

Some of the sort-ofs talked about going to law to have the will altered, but the lawyers said it was all very carefully drawn up and in any case no one could be sure who would get the money if they did get the will changed – it would probably have gone straight to the charities. So they decided to put up with it.

Almost at once Molly's parents realised this mightn't be too bad, after all. Barker needed a big garden to run about in, didn't he, and it happened there was this suitable house outside the town . . .

Molly said she'd go and see what Barker thought (though really she spent most of the time talking to Hannah). When she came back she said Barker wanted to stay in his own home, with Hannah to look after him, and Hannah didn't mind. (It was her home too – she'd lived there since she was sixteen.)

Molly's parents were *not* pleased and there was a real row, but Molly stuck to her guns. She kept saying Barker had made up his mind. Her father stormed off to the lawyers next morning, but they said the same thing. It was absolutely clear. If Molly said Barker wanted to stay in his own house, that was that. You may think it was tough-minded of Molly to stick it out, but she was a tough-minded girl. Perhaps that was why Mrs Barker had chosen her.

And she had something to help her. On the day the will had been read one of the lawyers had given her a letter and told her she wasn't to show it to anyone else. He hadn't even read it himself. It said:

My dear Molly,

You will now know the contents of my will. It is no doubt very selfish of me to amuse myself in this manner, but I am a selfish old person and that's that. When I was young I inherited a ridiculous amount of money, but it was all tied up in Trusts until I was twenty-five, so I got no fun out of it when I was a child. I have always resented this.

I see no reason why any of my connections should inherit my money. It will do far more good if it goes to charity, but it amuses me to think that before that a child might have some fun spending a little of it, as I never did. That is why I devised a little test to choose a child who was likely to be level-headed about money. I am glad it was you who passed the test.

If I were to leave the money to you till you are of age, people would insist on it being spent 'for your own good', and you would have very little say in the matter. That is why I have left it to Barker. My will says you are to be his guardian, but really it is the other way about. He is there to protect you – you are quite clever enough to see how useful he will be in this role. I strongly advise you to establish the point at the earliest possible moment.

Barker is an earnest soul (as I am not), and I think he will make a very good guardian.

Yours affectionately,
Ethelswitha Barker

So Molly did what the letter suggested and 'established the point'. She liked their own home, and so did her parents, really. The other one was much too grand for them, and after a few weeks her parents began to think so too.

But soon the other sort-ofs realised that Molly's family weren't the only ones who could suggest things Barker might like. They would stop Molly while she was taking him for one of his walks and say he looked a bit off-colour, and wouldn't a bit of sea-air do him good? Now it happened there was this holiday villa in Cornwall, a real snip, though he wouldn't want to use it all the time, would he, and maybe when he wasn't there it would be best if one of the Frossetts (or the McSniggs, or the Blounders, or the Globotzikoffs, or whichever of the sort-of families had thought of the scheme) went and took care of the place. For a suitable fee, perhaps.

Molly said Barker would think it over. The following week, she explained Barker thought he'd like to go on a rabbiting holiday this year, with Molly, of course, but he didn't want her to be lonely so she'd better bring a few friends and her Mum and Dad to drive him about to good rabbiting places. Barker paid for the petrol and the hotel rooms.

A bit later a new baby sort-of was born and had to be christened. Barker sent a silver napkin-ring, but without a name on it. Privately Molly wondered what would have happened if she'd told the silversmith to put 'Bonzo', but she explained that Barker didn't think it was quite right for a dog to tell people what to call their children.

And then one day in the supermarket Molly heard two mothers of sort-of families chatting about the old days, and the excitement of taking their children up to have tea with

Mrs Barker, and thinking of *really worthwhile* presents, and wondering whether by any chance little Sam or Betsy would be the one . . .

Molly talked to Barker about it on their next walk, and the upshot was that the notes started coming again, inviting the children to tea when it was their turn. It was a bit different, because Barker didn't ask questions the way Mrs Barker used to, and the food was better, and there was Molly to talk to and play with, but there was always camomile tea (or that's what Molly said it was, though it didn't taste much different from ordinary tea).

In fact it all became rather like an old custom, which people have forgotten the reason for, but go on doing because they've always done it and it's a bit picturesque and so on. And there were the presents, of course. They were as good as ever, but somehow it didn't seem quite so mean and grabby asking for them, which is what most people, in their heart of hearts, had probably felt, just as Molly had. And nobody now thought that Barker was going to leave all his money to a child who said 'Please' and 'Thank you' properly or an adult who turned up on the doorstep with a particularly nice present.

Mr Cyril Blounder, quite early on, did climb the steps one day with a bone he swore he'd dug up in his allotment, though it looked remarkably fresh. Hannah gave him camomile tea on the doorstep, and all the other sort-ofs felt he'd made a fool of himself and nobody else tried it.

Time passed. Nothing much new happened. Molly got older, and so did Barker. You'd have thought he was rather a dull dog if you met him, but he had interesting ideas. He longed to travel, Molly said, but he couldn't because of the quarantine, so instead he used to send Hannah and her sister who lived somewhere up in the North on annual holidays to exciting places, and Hannah would come back and show him her slides. He gave generously to charities on flag-days – not only to the RSPCA – and took a keen interest in nature preservation. He had some handsome trees planted in the park, with a bench under them which said:

IN FOND MEMORY OF ETHELSWITHA BARKER
Loving Mistress

Strangers didn't know quite what to make of that, but none of the local people thought it odd.

In fact one year there was a proposal to have Barker elected Mayor. It was only half-serious, of course, but it worried the real parties enough to pay lawyers to find out whether you can elect a dog Mayor, which you can't. But he might have got in. For a dull dog, he was surprisingly popular.

One lucky result from Barker's point of view was that he got quite an active love-life. In a town like that most people had pedigree dogs and used to send the bitches off to be mated. They tried to shoo mongrels away when their bitches were on heat, but it almost became a sort of status symbol to let your bitch have one litter of Barker's pups, so after a few years there were quite a lot of his children in the town – Barker's own sort-ofs. They weren't sort-ofs because their relationship with him was complicated, like Mrs Barker's had been. He was their father and they were his children. That was usually clear from the black-and-white patches. They were sort-of collies and sort-of Labradors and sort-of dachshunds and so on.

Curiously, people didn't mind having these mongrels born to their prize bitches, and even more curiously this wasn't because Barker was so rich – the didn't send the family a huge present when it happened, only the right number of collars, with names for the puppies on them. It was because the whole town was proud of having him around. He was odd, and different, and when nothing much was happening in the world reporters would come and write stories for their newspapers about him.

Of course they never got it quite right – reporters don't. It was difficult for them to understand the difference it made,

all that money belonging to a dog, and not a person. When old Mrs Barker had been alive people used to think about her money a lot, envying her or scheming how to wheedle cash out of her, or complaining about her not spending it on things they thought important. But somehow when the money belonged to a dog it stopped being so serious. There were still schemes and complaints, of course (you don't change people *that* much), but whoever was listening to the schemer or complainer was always likely to switch the conversation into jokes about Barker, almost as though the money wasn't real. It was, of course – it got trees planted and the spire repaired and it endowed nature trails and sent the over-60s on coach trips and bought a site for the Youth Club – but it didn't *matter* the way it had seemed to before. Even the sort-of families stopped being as spiteful about each other as they used to be – the money was out of everyone's reach now, so there wasn't much point.

Dogs don't live as long as humans, so it wasn't long before people started to fuss about Barker's health, and knit coats for him to wear in the winter – though he had a perfectly good thick coat of his own – and speak sharply to deliverymen who hurtled round corners in their vans. Barker was a fool about traffic. Of course Hannah was supposed to keep him locked in and Molly always fastened his lead when they were walking anywhere near roads, but if he saw a cat or smelt a rabbit there was absolutely no holding him, or he'd manage to slip out on one of his love-affairs while Hannah had the door open to take in the milk. The Town Council had notices put up at the most dangerous places, saying CAUTION: DOG CROSSING, but they weren't much use as Barker never crossed twice in the same place.

Still, he bore a charmed life for eight years. He had lots of narrow escapes. Strangers driving through sometimes hit lampposts or traffic islands trying to avoid him, and they couldn't understand why everybody was furious with *them*, and why there were always a dozen witnesses ready to come forward saying it was *their* fault.

The over-60s coach got him in the end – coming back from a trip Barker had paid for himself. Molly said that Barker had always wanted a really good send-off, so there was a jolly funeral with masses to eat and drink for the whole town, and a fun-fair and fireworks.

After that Molly spent a whole week with the lawyers, organising which charities should get Barker's money. Practically all of it went to ordinary sensible places, a bit to the RSPCA of course, but mostly things like Cancer Research and War on Want. But Molly kept one per cent aside (that doesn't sound very much, but Mrs Barker really had been enormously rich, so it was still a useful amount) for a special charity she had set up. The lawyers had had a lot of trouble making it legal, but she'd insisted it was what Barker wanted, so they managed it somehow.

That was why all the families in the town which had one of Barker's puppies as their pet got a surprise cheque through the letter box, with a letter saying it was to be spent exclusively for the benefit of their dog, and the youngest person in the house was the only one who could say what that dog wanted.

It was an idea that would have amused Mrs Barker, Molly thought, and made her wrinkle her lips into her sour little smile – sort-ofs getting something in the end. Only not her sort-ofs. Barker's.

FOCUS QUESTIONS

1 Why do Mrs Barker's 'sort-of' relatives bring her presents?

2 Explain the sentence: '*She* knew what they were thinking.'

3 Why do you think Mrs Barker would 'cross off one of the names in the back' of her notebook after she had been told what he or she wanted for a present?

4 Why does Mrs Barker ask Molly for one of the family dog's puppies for Christmas?

5 a What are the terms of Mrs Barker's will?
  b Why, according to the letter she wrote to Molly, had she written her will this way?

6 What are some of the 'interesting ideas' that Barker has?

7 a What happens to Mrs Barker's money when Barker (the dog) dies?
  b Why would Mrs Barker have been amused by this?

EXPLORING WORDS

8 Explain the meaning of the following underlined words and phrases from the story.
  a '. . . Hannah would bring him <u>camomile</u> tea.'
  b '. . . a pale blue frock with a white lacy apron <u>crackling new</u>.'
  c 'She <u>pursed</u> her purple lips.'
  d '. . . who did their best not to look too <u>triumphant</u>.'
  e '. . . I <u>devised</u> a little test to choose a child who was likely to be <u>level-headed</u> about money.'
  f '. . . and it's a bit <u>picturesque</u>.'
  g '. . . scheming how to <u>wheedle</u> cash out of her.'
  h '. . . it was to be spent <u>exclusively</u> for the benefit of their dog.'

WRITING

9   Write a story about another rich old person who does unusual things with his or her money. For example:

   ▶ Gives it away to people who do good deeds.

   ▶ Sets up a shop with the aim of losing money.

DISCUSSION

10 Your class inherits $250,000 from Mrs Barker. You must decide – in a democratic way – what to do with it. Everybody in the class must be happy with the way in which decisions are made.

Thanks for Nothing

A t times like this, Ronnie went outside and talked to the dog. He didn't know what he'd do without Boz. Most likely shout and kick and throw things like some of the other kids he knew.

Boz sat beside Ronnie on the bricks and listened. He never yapped. He never answered back. And when Ronnie had poured out all his troubles, Boz leaned forward and licked the tears from his cheeks.

If Ronnie ever left home, he'd take Boz with him. The way he felt now, he'd leave home any day. This minute. Never mind that he didn't have a place to go. Never mind that he had very little money. Never mind his mother, the schoolteachers, the police.

If his mother would leave him alone, things would be a whole lot better. But she was at him all day – nag, nag, nag, pick, pick, pick. No wonder the old man shot through.

This latest row was about money. Again. She didn't even want him to spend his own wages. He'd been doing a paper round since he was nine. Nearly four years now. 'I don't know where it all goes, Ronnie,' she said. 'You never save a bean.' Well, it was *his* money, wasn't it? It was he that got up at 5.30 in the morning, six days a week. It was he that pedalled around in the dark and got cold and wet and set upon by dogs.

He put an arm around Boz's neck. The dog didn't move, but sat there as if to show he was something that could be leaned upon. Solid old kelpie; reliable old black; greying now but rock solid.

Ronnie looked around the yard that was not big enough to do a Lillee or even half a Lillee. His mother's attempts at gardening were showing promise. The plant with frilled leaves had a few red flowers and a crawling vine almost covered the Margottinis' fence. Little things were sprouting in pots and funny-smelling yellow flowers smothered a bush at the back door. He knew the name of that one. Daisy. And he had to admit, it didn't look bad.

He heard the clink of the gate and footsteps around the side of the house and he knew it was Spider.

'What you doing?' asked Spider.

'Nothing,' said Ronnie.

'Yeah, looks like it. You got any money?'

'I got paid this morning.'

'Good.'

Spider walked around the yard and banged the picket fences with his first, as if he were casing the joint. Spider was big and lean and wore an earring. He reckoned he was getting a tattoo next week. He'd picked out the design – a girl with a snake around her waist – and he was going back when he had the money.

'You coming down the mall?' said Spider.

The window rattled and Mrs Trott pushed her head through the opening. 'You're not going out, are you Ronnie?'

'Why?' he called back.

'Because tea's early and I want you to clean up inside.'

'But it's Saturday, Mum.'

'You want to waste all your money again?'

Ronnie stared at the bricks. 'Not really, but . . .'

'Good then, I'll get tea.' The rumble of trucks along Barkly Street drowned out the clatter as Mrs Trott closed the window.

'There you go,' said Spider. 'Gated again.'

'Well,' said Ronnie, 'there's not much to do, anyhow.'

'We could go to the pinnies.'

'That'd really set Mum going.'

'You're a bore, Ronnie.' Spider took another turn around the yard. 'Don't know why I bother with you.'

Ronnie was scared Spider would go. He wanted him to stay. He wanted to be part of the gang, one of Spider's mates. 'Where is everyone?' he asked.

'Down at the pinnies. They've got a new game there – Galaxial Serpent. Ace!'

Ronnie groaned. He really wanted to play that new game and he did have enough money for a bit of fun.

The back door opened and Mrs Trott propped the fly-wire open with her hip. 'Will you feed Boz, Ronnie?'

Spider spoke to Ronnie out of the corner of his mouth. 'Tell her you're having tea at my joint. Tell her you're staying the night.'

Ronnie hesitated.

'Go on, tell her.'

Ronnie looked at his mother, but not into her eyes. 'Spider says I can have tea at his place – and stay the night.'

'What does his mother say?'

'Fine, fine,' said Spider.

'Well, I suppose it's all right, as long as you're home early tomorrow.'

Spider dug Ronnie in the ribs when Mrs Trott went back inside. 'Easy, eh?'

'What's your mother going to say?' said Ronnie.

'Nothing. She'll say O.K., I can stay with you.'

'What do you mean?'

'You're staying with me and I'm staying with you. Neat. Get it?'

Ronnie nodded slowly. 'Yeah, I get it. And what are we going to do?'

'Go down the mall, to the pinnies, meet the gang, have a time.'

'Gee, Spider.' Spider was great on ideas. 'Where do we sleep then?'

'We don't.'

Ronnie didn't ask any more questions. He went to his bedroom and took his money from the top drawer. 'G'bye, Mum,' he said. 'See you tomorrow.' He and Spider set off down the street and around the corner to Spider's place. They didn't hear Mrs Trott calling out that he'd forgotten his pyjamas.

Spider's mother was not home when they arrived. Spider left a note in the kitchen to say he was spending the night at Ronnie's place. He reckoned she wouldn't worry, anyway.

They went to the fish and chips shop and met up with Jake and Stretch and Lennie. Spider ordered a hamburger with the lot and Ronnie paid for it. He asked for fish and chips for himself and the others had souvlaki. They ate from the paper wrapping as they walked along the mall. Around the corner, at the amusement centre, they pulled handles and pressed buttons and jabbed each other in the ribs until closing time.

'I'm flat,' said Spider. 'Could you lend us a bit, Ronnie?'

Ronnie gave him his last dollar. Spider bought smokes and Ronnie had a couple because he liked the feel of it, more than the taste of them. Spider told the others about the tattoo he was planning. Stretch said it was best not to get one high up on the arm, because in winter nobody could see it. Spider said yeah, he planned it for just above the wrist.

'Mum would never come at a tattoo,' said Ronnie. 'I reckon she'd cut my ear off if I even had an earring.'

They all jeered. 'Wondered why you looked so underdressed,' said Stretch. Stretch looked good with an earring because his face was skinny like a jug that needed a handle.

When they'd all run out of money, Jake said he'd go home because he was racing at the bike track next morning. Lennie went with him. Spider said they could find some action down by the wharves, but Stretch said he wasn't walking that far. Ronnie nodded to Spider and said he was no jibber. He'd go wherever Spider wanted.

If they went across the road, said Spider, they might get a nip from one of the old men who hung around the benches there.

Ronnie wondered how Spider knew so much. After Jake and Lennie left, Stretch and Ronnie and Spider strolled across to the park. The old men had gone or were asleep somewhere else. Spider said O.K., they might as well bunk down themselves.

This was a real night out, thought Ronnie. He wished he'd worn his duffle coat. And a pillow would be nice. The ground was cold and hard and the grass brushed his skin like a damp face-washer.

Stretch lay down and went out like a light. Spider leaned on one elbow and talked on about rotten school and rotten home and the tattoo of the girl with the snake. Ronnie listened and wondered what time it was. When the black night sky began to lighten and he could make out the lines of the overhead railway bridge, he asked if it was time to go. His legs ached. He didn't think he'd slept at all.

They walked home the long way, in case anyone had dropped money in the carparks during the night. Nobody had. Stretch left them at the corner of Pickett Street and Spider and Ronnie went on to Spider's house for breakfast.

Spider's mother was sitting at the bench in a baggy pink dressing gown. 'Don't they serve breakfast at the Trotts' place?' she asked as Spider went through the kitchen cupboard.

Spider grunted and pulled out a packet of cornflakes. Ronnie stared at the milk carton and was grateful when the telephone rang.

Spider's mother dragged towards it. 'Yes,' she said, picking up the receiver. 'Yes, he's here. You want him home? O.K., I'll tell him.' She signalled to Ronnie that his mother wanted him. 'What's that?' she said into the mouthpiece. 'Don't thank *me* – thank you for having Spider. You didn't? They didn't? No, they weren't here.' She raised her eyebrows at Spider. 'No, they were not. Only just come in.'

'Uh, uh,' thought Ronnie. 'Now I'm in for it.'

Spider's mother put the telephone down and pointed to Ronnie. 'You'd better go,' she said.

Ronnie left his cornflakes untouched and bolted towards the door. 'Thanks for having me,' he said which he thought was pretty stupid when he'd only been there two minutes.

Now he was really in a spot. Now was the time to shoot through. Now – except for one thing. He couldn't leave without Boz.

The street was still as he slammed the little gate. He turned in the direction of home and decided he would collect Boz and his jacket and leave home. He couldn't face his mother now. He'd not only told a lie. He'd blown a whole week's pay.

His mind made up, he walked steadily along the footpath. He would go in the door quietly. With luck, his mother might be in the shower. He'd slip in and out and get going before she caught him. He'd have to be quick. He could just see her, red-faced and storming. 'Where have you been, Ronnie?' And before he had a chance to answer, she'd jump in with something like: 'spent all your money, I bet. And look at you! A disgrace!'

He knew his jeans were dirty and his sweater was crushed and damp. He didn't know what his face looked like.

He reached the house and stepped over the gate. Everything was quiet and his sneakers made no sound on the bricks. He walked around the side towards the back door. He opened the flywire door and peeped inside.

His mother was standing beside the kitchen table. She stood there and looked at him and her face was not red and storming, but pale and tired and older than he'd noticed before.

'Hello,' he said, shakily.

Boz uncurled on the linoleum floor and scratched towards Ronnie. He leaped and barked as if to ask what had happened. Ronnie pushed Boz down. His eyes were still on his mother.

She stepped towards him and didn't ask where he had been all night. 'You look hungry, Ronnie,' she said. 'Come and have breakfast.'

'Yes Mum, I'm hungry,' he said. 'And I'm cold.'

FOCUS QUESTIONS

1 Why is Ronnie feeling depressed?

2 Why is Ronnie so dependent on Boz?

3 What is your first impression of Spider?

4 Why is Ronnie afraid that Spider will go to the 'pinnies' without him?

5 In how many different ways do both Spider and Stretch take advantage of Ronnie?

6 Do you think Ronnie enjoys what he originally thought of as 'a real night out'?

7 Why is Ronnie undecided about whether or not to go home?

8 How do you explain the 'unexpected' reaction of Ronnie's mother when he arrives home?

9 Now that you have finished reading the story, can you explain why the writer might have included the paragraph beginning with the lines: 'Ronnie looked around the yard . . .'?

10 What are your thoughts about the story's title? Is it a good one? Can you suggest other possibilities?

WRITING

11 Write the dialogue (conversation) that takes place when Spider calls at Ronnie's house on the following Saturday.

12 'Leaving Home.' Use this as the title of an original story of your own.

Jack and the Beanstalk

Jack's mother said, 'We're *stony broke*!
'Go out and find some wealthy bloke
'Who'll buy our cow. Just say she's sound
'And worth at least a hundred pound.
'But don't you dare to let him know
'That she's as old as billy-o.'
Jack led the old brown cow away,
And came back later in the day,
And said, 'Oh mumsie dear, guess what
'Your clever little boy has got.
'I got, I really don't know how,
'A super trade-in for our cow.'
The mother said, 'You little creep
'I'll bet you sold her much too cheap.'
When Jack produced one lousy bean,
His startled mother, turning green,
Leaped high up in the air and cried,
'I'm *absolutely stupefied*!
'You crazy boy! D'you really mean
'You sold our Daisy for a bean?'
She snatched the bean. She yelled, 'You chump!'
And flung it on the rubbish-dump.
Then summoning up all her power,
She beat the boy for half an hour,

Using (and nothing could be meaner)
The handle of a vacuum-cleaner.
At ten p.m. or thereabout,
The little bean began to sprout.
By morning it had grown so tall
You couldn't see the top at all.
Young Jack cried, 'Mum, admit it now!
'It's better than a rotten cow!'
The mother said, 'You lunatic!
'Where are the beans that I can pick?
'There's not *one bean*! It's bare as bare!'
'No no!' cried Jack. 'You look up there!
'Look very high and you'll behold
'Each single leaf is solid gold!'
By gollikins, the boy was right!
Now, glistening in the morning light,
The mother actually perceives
A mass of lovely golden leaves!
She yells out loud, 'My sainted souls!
'I'll sell the Mini, buy a Rolls!
'Don't stand and gape, you little clot!
'Get up there quick and grab the lot!'
Jack was nimble, Jack was keen.
He scrambled up the mighty bean.
Up up he went without a stop,
But just as he was near the top,
A ghastly frightening thing occurred —
Not far above his head he heard
A big deep voice, a rumbling thing
That made the very heavens ring.

It shouted loud, 'FEE FI FO FUM
'I SMELL THE BLOOD OF AN ENGLISHMAN!'
Jack was frightened, Jack was quick,
And down he climbed in half a tick.
'Oh mum!' he gasped. 'Believe you me
'There's something nasty up our tree!
'I saw him, mum! My gizzard froze!
'A Giant with a clever nose!'
'A *clever nose!*' his mother hissed.
'You must be going round the twist!'
'He smelled me out, I swear it, mum!
'He said he *smelled* an Englishman!'
The mother said, 'And well he might!
'I've told you every single night
'To take a bath because you smell,
'But would you do it? Would you hell!
'You even make your mother shrink
'Because of your unholy stink!'
Jack answered, 'Well, if you're so clean
'Why don't *you* climb the crazy bean.'
The mother cried, 'By gad, I will!
'There's life within the old dog still!'
She hitched her skirts above her knee
And disappeared right up the tree.
Now would the Giant smell his mum?
Jack listened for the *fee-fo-fum.*
He gazed aloft. He wondered when
The dreaded words would come . . . And then . . .
From somewhere high above the ground
There came a frightful crunching sound.
He heard the Giant mutter twice,
'By gosh, that tasted very nice.
'Although' (and this in grumpy tones)
'I wish there weren't so many bones.'
'By Christopher!' Jack cried. 'By gum!
'The Giant's eaten up my mum!

'He smelled her out! She's in his belly!
'I had a hunch that she was smelly.'
Jack stood there gazing longingly
Upon the huge and golden tree.
He murmured softly, 'Golly-gosh,
'I guess I'll *have* to take a wash
'If I am going to climb this tree
'Without the Giant smelling me.
'In fact, a bath's my only hope . . .'
He rushed indoors and grabbed the soap
He scrubbed his body everywhere.
He even washed and rinsed his hair.
He did his teeth, he blew his nose
And went out smelling like a rose.
Once more he climbed the mighty bean.
The Giant sat there, gross, obscene,
Muttering through his vicious teeth
(While Jack sat tensely just beneath),
Muttering loud, 'FEE FI FO FUM,
'RIGHT NOW I CAN'T SMELL ANYONE.'
Jack waited till the Giant slept,
Then out along the boughs he crept
And gathered so much gold, I swear
He was an instant millionaire.
'A bath,' he said, 'does seem to pay.
'I'm going to have one every day.'

FOCUS QUESTIONS

1   Why does Jack's mother tell him to sell their cow?

2   Why is Jack's mother so angry with him when he returns?

3   When she realises the beanstalk is sprouting gold leaves at its top, how does her attitude change?

4   What do we learn about Jack's mother when he climbs down the beanstalk without any gold?

5   Does Jack's mother deserve her fate? Give reasons.

WRITING

6   Write a sequel to this story and describe what Jack does with his newly acquired wealth.

7   Write your own modern version of an old fairy-tale or nursery rhyme.

8   Arrange a dramatic reading of 'Jack and the Beanstalk'. Give parts to a narrator, Jack, his mother and the giant.

No Christmas for Ben

*I*n those last minutes of fading light silvering the creek surface, the trout rose from its secret darkness like a leviathan. Ben saw the enormous jaws take the frog on his line.

'Oh God, let me get it. It's the biggest fish I've ever seen. I've got to catch it.' Frog gently held in its mouth, the dark shadow turned downstream towards the overhanging wall.

'I'll have to strike now, and it could be too soon. But if I don't it'll get under the blackberries and break the line.' Ben struck as hard as he could. When the weight came onto his arms he thought the trout was gone and he had his hook into a log. Then he felt the great surge downstream and let out line, quickly. A six-pound breaking strain wouldn't hold this fish. He'd have to tire it out properly and that might take hours. If only he could keep it away from the banks and in the middle of the creek.

'I've got to stay calm. I've got to wear it down.' Slowly the boy brought the tip of his rod up, half expecting it to break, but again there was a kind of flurry near the surface and the great trout was coming back towards Ben, who reeled in fast. An inch of slack would be the end. Slowly the fish came closer, almost under the bridge from which Ben was fishing, before it turned and ran downstream again. The boy felt that if he could take this fish home and show them he wouldn't care if he never caught another thing in his whole life. Once more Ben managed to turn the trout before it reached the downstream corner where the concrete jutted out. The fish felt pain deep in its jaw where the hook penetrated, pain which got worse all the time. Once more the trout let itself be guided by that pain and turned obediently when the boy tightened the line.

But it was the last time. When Ben tried to turn the fish downstream it shook itself like a wet dog and swam near the far bank where the blackberries grew low into the water. Perhaps the line tightened too suddenly, or perhaps the small hook worked free. All Ben knew was that the weight was gone, the top of his rod was broken and lying on the bridge, and the line was free. If he hadn't been almost twelve, Ben would have cried.

'No one's ever going to believe me,' he said aloud. 'There's never been a trout as big as this in the creek before.'

'I'll tell them about it, boy,' and old Harry Wilson, who lived in the second hut down the road, stood up.

'How long've you been there?'

'All the time, boy. That was a whale you hooked. Bad luck you couldn't land it.'

'Not bad luck at all. It was this lousy gear. You can't catch anything decent on this kind of tackle. Dad says I can't have a proper rod yet. It isn't fair. You know, Harry, I would've got that fish if I'd had a decent rod with a bit of give in it. This one never was any good.'

'Now steady on, boy. Given the best rod in the world you'd have to be lucky to land a big fish here. The creek's too narrow and too full of snags. You did well to turn it like you did. That was a mighty big trout. Why, I don't reckon you really felt its full weight. It could just about pull you in.' But Ben kicked his broken rod angrily. He still thought he could've held the fish if his rod had been better. One thing was good. Old Harry would tell them there really was a monster in the creek. They'd never believe him.

After he'd told about the trout, Ben asked his father to get him a decent rod for Christmas. That wouldn't be long to wait. It was almost December now. The fish might hang about for a few weeks longer. But his father wouldn't listen.

'You want too much, Ben,' he said. 'You know things haven't been too good this year, and your mother and sisters need more than fishing tackle. Why don't you get a good willow switch and put runners on it? I used one until I was twenty, and caught some fine fish on it, too. I'm sorry, Ben, but that's the way it is this year.'

'It isn't fair,' and Ben went down to the bridge to try and see the big one again. He wondered if it felt pain from the hook. Fish weren't supposed to feel much but he guessed they did. Perhaps, as his father said, everything has its own kind of pain. Perhaps even trees felt something when they were cut down. But, pain or not, he wanted to catch that fish and he couldn't do it without good tackle. He knew just the rod. Solid and easy to grip at the base, and thin as a whip at the tapered end. He had to have it. If Christmas wasn't so close he might have managed it. He knew he had over twenty dollars in his money box, but that was supposed to be kept for birthday and Christmas presents. They all got pocket money but only some of it could be spent. Earlier in the year there would have been more time to save money. But he had to have the rod. He just had to. He didn't care about Christmas and presents. Ben thought that if he couldn't get the rod in the Sports Shop he'd run away or something. He had to have it.

He knew when he took the money from the box that his father would be angry about it. Well, he'd just have to be angry, that's all. Perhaps when he caught the big trout they'd give him some more Christmas money. He didn't care about presents. All he wanted was the rod.

After he'd paid for the rod and a decent reel there was only a dollar left for Christmas.

'I don't care. I'll be able to get that old trout now,' he thought exultantly. Ben felt happy taking the rod home. Now let the big fellow watch out. It wasn't until he was almost inside that he realised he couldn't very well show them the rod. He'd have to hide it and use it in the evenings when his father wasn't about. He knew he should tell them what he'd done but he couldn't. Not yet. Not until he'd caught the trout. Once they saw it they'd know why he'd bought the rod. Often people didn't understand what was important and what wasn't. He couldn't have waited until next year, when the fish might be miles away.

When Ben used the new rod he discovered it wasn't so easy. The old stiff one had been long enough to almost drop the frog where he wanted it to go. The shorter rod, whippy and lighter, wasn't much good. After he'd lost his third hook and frog on the blackberries Ben went home. He was beginning to realise that he'd need a lot of practice to handle that rod properly.

Later that week, old Harry called him over to the hut.

'Come here, boy. I want to show you something.' The old man had a new fishing rod, a beauty. Not quite as flexible as Ben's new rod, but the runners were better and the varnish was smoother, kind of deeper.

'Gosh, that's a beauty, Harry. Where did you get it?'

'It's yours, boy. I was going to keep it until Christmas but thought you might like a go at the big one before then. That fish won't stay forever and I'd like to see you land him. I did all the bindings myself and I can guarantee they'd hold a whale. Take it, boy. But next time you go fishing, don't forget to take a gaff. A trout that size wouldn't fit into a landing net.' Ben's lips felt stiff and swollen like after a visit to the dentist. His mouth was too dry to say anything.

'Thanks, Harry. Thanks.' That's all he could say. Whatever would he do with the other rod? Perhaps someone would buy it from him. He knew the store wouldn't take it back because the varnish was scratched and the cork grip was blood-stained from a cut.

Ben walked home slowly, Harry's rod smooth and cool in his hand. He felt bad. Now the empty money box was worse than anything in the world. When he got home they were all in the big kitchen.

'What's that you've got, Ben?'

'Harry Wilson gave it to me for Christmas.'

'Let me see it. That's a good rod. You'll never meet a trout that rod can't handle. Now you've got this, you'll need a good reel and line and perhaps your mother and I will be able to manage things so you'll get them this year after all. It'd be a pity to put cheap tackle on a rod like that.'

Ben couldn't think of anything to say.

'You're not in trouble are you, son? You should be looking forward to a pretty good Christmas, getting something you wanted so much.

'Is there anything wrong, Ben? Come on, out with it.'

But Ben couldn't say anything. Holding tight so he wouldn't make a fool of himself, the boy walked into his bedroom. As he left the big kitchen he heard his father say:

'What's wrong with him? He must be ill. He's wanted a good rod ever since he caught his first fish. And now look at him. A real picture of misery if ever I've seen one.'

Ben couldn't hear what his mother said. Whatever any of them said couldn't make any difference. He didn't know what to do. He couldn't tell them but he knew he had to before they found out. One dollar wasn't enough to buy anything for Mum and the girls, let alone his father. Even Grandma wouldn't get her usual box of chocolates. Ben's chest hurt. There was pain in it . . . bad pain. He didn't feel well. Perhaps he'd die and that would be the very best thing that could happen. He knew he'd never catch the big trout. He didn't even want to. All he could think of was that now he had two beautiful fishing rods . . . and no Christmas at all.

FOCUS QUESTIONS

1 Explain the meaning of the following phrase: ' . . . the trout rose from its secret darkness like a leviathan.'

2 Why does Ben think he will need to thoroughly exhaust the fish if he is to have any chance of catching it?

3 Ben blames his tackle (gear) for his failure to catch 'anything decent', but Harry disagrees and suggests other reasons. Are you more inclined to agree with Harry or Ben?

4 Why does Ben's father dismiss his wish to be given a decent rod at Christmas?

5 Where does Ben obtain the money he needs to buy the rod he has always wanted?

6 Why is Ben initially disappointed with the new rod?

7 Why is Ben both overjoyed and very unhappy at the same time when Harry gives him a new fishing rod?

8 Why does Ben believe that he will never catch the big trout, and why does he have no deep longing to do so anyway?

WRITING AND DISCUSSION

9 If you were in Ben's situation, what would you do?

10 Write (or talk about) the next 'chapter' of this story, describing how you think Ben might be able to make things better for everybody, solve his problems and have a good Christmas.

Water Melons

*T*he sun poured down heat and the hot summer wind was blowing. It blew dust into men's eyes and bad temper into their hearts. Grandad Kostas and Uncle Petros were playing cards in the taverna, the village cafe. They had played and got excited and argued together many times before. Today was different. Petros was winning. The hot wind blew. Grandad Kostas felt ill and savage.

Suddenly he slammed his cards on the table. He put his head forward like a snake and spat the word, 'Cheat!'

The eyes of Uncle Petros bulged with shock.

'Cheat?' he whispered.

'You have been cheating,' said Grandad Kostas in a voice as cold as death. Uncle Petros pointed a finger at him, trembling with hurt feelings and rage.

'I am an honest man,' he rasped. 'No one . . . no one,' he struggled. 'No one calls me a cheat!'

'You are a crook,' Grandad accused. 'I have always known it.'

'In the old days,' Petros menaced him, 'men died for words like that.'

Grandad looked him up and down and made a sneering noise.

'Yes!' Petros made a stabbing movement with his fist. He

took a deep breath and lowered his hand. 'But you . . . you . . . bah! You're too old and silly and feeble. You're safe.'

'Feeble!' Grandad growled the word so hard that he made himself cough. The veins stood out on his head as he fought for breath.

'Weak in body and mind,' Petros insisted. He screwed a finger into the side of his head. 'Your brain is soft. You have become a child again. I've known it for some time. I'm sorry for you. Pah!' He flicked his fingers in Grandad's face, glared for a moment and stalked off.

'Child!' coughed Grandad. He went after Petros so fast that he nearly fell over a chair. Wincing, he picked himself up and held on to the chair, coughing again. When he got his breath back, he stared round like a wounded bull. The others in the cafe looked quickly away. Grandad stiffened his back and walked home.

There he stalked in past his daughter, Christina, and his grandson, Tassos. He went through into his bedroom and lay down. Christina followed him.

'Aren't you feeling well?' she asked. 'I told you not to go out with that cough.'

He looked at her in silence, showing his teeth. She went out again, making a face, and sent Tassos out to see what had happened.

When he came back with the story, she said, 'Men!' and carried on about the trouble it would cause. Tassos had already foreseen this but he listened politely.

They lived in a small Greek village called Mikrokhorio. Tassos' father was away in America, working to send money home. He couldn't send a lot but Grandad Kostas had a plot of land on which he grew vegetables and water melons. Selling the melons gave them enough money to live through the year without too much worry. They needed a lorry, however, to get the melons to the nearest town. The melons were ripe and ready and there were three or four lorry loads in the crop. Unfortunately, Uncle Petros had the only lorry in the area.

The market was waiting. Left too long the melons would begin to rot. Christina didn't think too long about it. She sent Tassos to see Uncle Petros who was not a real uncle but who had known Tassos since he was a baby.

Petros was calm but coldly polite. He said he could hardly allow the lorry, under the circumstances, to help Grandad out. However, if Grandad would make a full apology, he, Petros, would think about it.

Tassos brought the message back and they went in to see Grandad. He was quite short with them. There was no way in which, he said, he was going to apologise to any lying cheat who had so insulted him. He, Grandad, would see him, Petros, in Hell first.

Tassos did not take this message to Petros.

His mother did not say much after that. Tassos could tell, though, from the way she bit her lip and banged things about that she was not happy. He thought it wise to get outside and have a look round the yard.

After a while he came back in. 'Grisoula,' he said.

'Dear God!' His mother clutched her heart. 'Not the donkey! What's wrong with the donkey?'

'Nothing,' he said. 'But I could use it to take the melons to Kastro.' She stared at him and then she scowled.

'You?' she flared up. 'Take the melons to town? On the donkey? How many melons do you think it can carry? Ten? Twenty? What good is that? There are thousands of melons! Millions! I've never heard anything so stupid in my life. What are you talking about?'

Tassos shrugged. 'What else?' he said.

'Do you know how many kilometres it is to Kastro?' she went on. 'Sixteen? More. And over the mountain road! It would take you all day. It would be afternoon before you got there. There'd be nobody about to buy them.' She ran down for a moment.

'I'd go by the mountain track,' he said. 'It's steeper but shorter. I'd start well before dawn and be in Kastro by morning. I could carry some melons, too, in a sack.'

'Impossible!' she snorted and he went out again to let her think it over.

That afternoon she helped him to gather enough water melons to fill two large bags for Grisoula and a smaller one for himself. He was up about three in the morning and on his way shortly after that.

It was a long, dreary slog up the mountain in the dark. Grisoula helped, never stopping and moving almost as if she could see. It was tough going for Tassos, though, guided only by the thin light of the torch and unbalanced by the sack. When dawn came, things were easier and he was well down the other side. In Kastro he didn't go to market but stood on a street corner to sell the melons. By afternoon they had all gone and he could start the long plod back.

The next trip was harder. He couldn't stop yawning as he loaded Grisoula in the silent early morning. He stumbled often and fell once on the steep upward track. Luckily, when it grew light and he could look properly, he had only damaged two of his melons. Even those he sold cheaply in Kastro. Bargaining

with customers kept him awake but he was very weary on the way home.

On the third morning he felt better. In Kastro the melons went as well as they had done before and he and Grisoula came back to the village at their usual time. Uncle Petros was waiting for him at the top of the village street. He looked very serious.

'Tasso!' He shook his head.

'What?' said Tassos.

'Every morning you go to Kastro. Every afternoon you walk back. It's killing work. You're only a boy – a child. You'll make yourself ill.'

'We haven't got a lorry,' Tassos said.

'You can have a lorry!' Uncle Petros waved his hands in the air. 'One word and you can have my lorry. That's all. Let Kostas admit that he was stupid and wrong – let him humble himself – and the lorry is his.'

'He won't do that,' Tassos told him.

'He will have to see sense. I am a man of honour,' Petros urged. 'Such insults have been wiped out in blood before now. I can't ignore it. I will not ignore it! He must take it back – say he's truly sorry.'

'I know,' Tassos agreed.

'He must see that there is no other way out. And he must be worried. Every day that he waits makes it worse for him. Those water melons must be got to market. It's urgent. They'll spoil. They'll rot!'

'I'm taking some of them,' Tassos pointed out.

'Ah!' Petros snapped. 'That's it. Don't you see that you're helping him in his wicked foolishness? While you take the melons to market he feels he can defy me. You must stop these journeys. Then he'll come to me. He'll apologise. Everything will be all right.'

Tassos shrugged, smothering a yawn.

'Otherwise . . .' Petros wagged a finger under his nose, 'I'll wash my hands of you. You'll be sorry then. Tomorrow . . . stay at home! You must!'

Tassos shrugged again in a way that might have meant anything and went on his way home. Petros stood, hands on hips, glaring after him.

As he tied up and fed Grisoula, Tassos thought about it. He would never get all the melons to market. Grandad had started the quarrel and Uncle Petros had some right on his side. There was justice, though, and there was family. Grandad was family and Uncle Petros wasn't. Grandad could make up his own mind. He, Tassos, knew what he had to do.

Next day he toiled again over the mountain to Kastro. When he came back, he saw Uncle Petros sitting in the taverna watching him. Neither of them spoke. Petros was there again the next day.

In the early hours of the following morning, Tassos came down to the dark yard, yawning and scratching his head. Then something shocked him wide awake. He flashed his torch round.

'Grisoula?' he said. But she had gone. He was angry with her at first until he found no rope. She could hardly have untied herself.

It was not easy to track her down. Her smudged footprints in the dust were difficult to see in the torch light. Her trail led out of the village, away from the track to Kastro and up another mountainside where few people ever went. There all sign of her disappeared. He had given up hope of finding her when he heard someone swear. He went towards where the sound had come from.

'Who's there?' he asked, shining his torch. It showed him Uncle Petros.

'Ah!' said Uncle Petros, blinking and smiling falsely. 'Tasso! I'm glad it's you.' He didn't sound glad.

'Where's Grisoula?' Tassos asked.

'Grisoula?' said Petros, as if he didn't quite understand. There was a clop of small hooves. Hearing Tassos' voice, Grisoula had come to find him, dragging her rope. 'Oh! Gris*ooula*!' admitted Uncle Petros. 'She must have got loose. I couldn't sleep. When I got up and looked through my window, I saw her wandering in the village.'

'I see.' Tassos nodded.

'I didn't bring her home,' Petros explained. 'I thought, if I chanced to make a noise in the darkness, you might be alarmed. It could have made more trouble, you see. I thought it best to wait until it was light.'

'Why bring her here up the mountain?' Tassos asked. He held Grisoula's rope and patted her neck.

'Here? Ah! Yes. Well . . .' Petros stopped, clearing his throat. 'I thought . . .' He cleared his throat thoroughly and went on, 'I thought she might be wandering, looking for food. I thought I'd pass the time bringing her here to find some food or something for her.'

'There's not much for a donkey to eat up here,' Tassos told him.

'No,' Petros agreed. 'I'd begun to realise that.'

There was silence until Tassos said, 'Why are you sitting down there by that rock?'

Petros did not answer at once. Then he said with a kind of laugh, 'I slipped. Dropped the torch when I fell down here and twisted my knee. I can't walk.'

'Oh dear,' said Tassos.

He found the dropped torch. With difficulty he got Petros on to Grisoula's back and led her down the mountain. He could hear Petros grunting with pain and swearing from time to time. He took him home and woke Aunty Eleni, Petros' wife. She and Tassos helped Uncle Petros into the house. Then Tassos went home, loaded Grisoula and set off for Kastro.

He was much later getting back that day. Uncle Petros, propped on two walking-sticks in the shade of a tree, was waiting for him well before he reached the village.

'Now Tasso,' he said.

'Uncle,' Tassos greeted him.

'I've got two men to pick your melon crop,' Uncle Petros told him. 'They've been loading the lorry this afternoon. You'll get the rest of your crop to market before the end of the week.'

'Ah!' said Tassos. 'And Grandad?'

'I haven't spoken to him yet, I've been waiting here for you most of the afternoon.' Petros looked at the ground and cleared his throat. 'About this morning . . . nobody saw us going home. It was too dark. People think I sprained my leg in an accident in the house. Nobody needs to know what really happened. No sense in shouting it about.'

'No,' Tassos agreed.

'Good.' Petros looked relieved. 'You're a good lad. A wise man knows when to speak and when to keep silent. Glad you see it my way. I shan't forget it.'

'You can rely on me, Uncle,' Tassos told him and went home.

Grandad had been looking for Petros for some time, eager to apologise. When Tassos told him where Petros could be found, he hurried off.

Tassos fed Grisoula, got himself something to eat and then sat outside with her in the evening cool. His grandfather came in sight, helping Petros along the street. The two old men stopped in the taverna.

'Look at them!' Tassos sniffed. His legs ached and his shoulder hurt. 'Grandad should have known better. But – Uncle Petros! Stealing you to hide you away and stop us going to Kastro!' Tassos wriggled his sore feet. 'He is a twister!' he went on bitterly. 'Someone should tell him so. I've a good mind to go and tell him myself now!'

Grisoula turned her head and gazed at him with wise, brown eyes. Being only a donkey, she, of course, said nothing.

He looked at her and then beyond at the mountains. The sun had gone down. The evening sky was a gentle violet colour and peaceful. Tassos relaxed. He could sleep late tomorrow. He didn't need to go to Kastro. He could do what he liked.

'Yes, Grisoula,' he said. 'You're quite right.'

FOCUS QUESTIONS

1 What effect did the wind have on people?

2 What happened in the old days when one person accused another of being dishonest?

3 What does Uncle Petros mean when he says that Grandad Kostas has 'become a child again'?

4 Why does Tassos suggest that the produce be taken to the market on the donkey and what is his mother's initial reaction to this suggestion?

5 What makes the journey to and from Kastro very difficult for Tassos?

6 Why does Uncle Petros insist that Grandad apologise to him?

7 Explain Grisoula's disappearance.

8 Petros' accident on the mountain could be seen as 'the turning point' in the story. Do you agree? Give reasons.

9 Explain, in some detail, the last line of the story: 'Yes, Grisoula,' he said. 'You're quite right.'

10 What are your final impressions and opinions of Grandad Kostas and Uncle Petros?

WRITING

11 Write a story of your own based on one of the following sayings:
 ▶ A wise person knows when to speak and when to keep silent.
 ▶ One good turn deserves another.
 ▶ All's well that ends well.